Home
ECONOMICS
for Northern Ireland

Anne Scott

Kathryn Wheeler

Doris Torrens

Pamela Mark

Hodder Murray

A MEMBER OF THE HODDER HEADLINE GROUP

Acknowledgements

The authors and publishers would like to thank the following companies, institutions and individuals who have given permission to reproduce copyright materials. The publisher would be happy to make arrangements with any copyright holders whom it has not been possible to contact.

The illustrations were drawn by Tim Beer, Maggie Brand, Ann Johns, and Ann Kronheimer

Photographs   Biophoto Associates/Science Photo Library (71 left & middle), British Electrotechnical Approvals Board (140), British Standards Institution (140), CC Studio/Science Photo Library (6 right), Citizens Advice Bureau (137), Consumers' Association (137), Creda Ltd//David Cave Photography (126 all, 127), Tim Fisher/Life File (60), Health Education Authority (64), HJ Heinz Co Ltd (143), Hodder Photo Library (73, 114 bottom, 115 bottom, 121 bottom right), Home Laundering Consultative Council (139), Crispin Hughes/Photofusion (56 left), Kenwood (118 bottom, 119 all, 121 bottom left 122 all, 123 all), Emma Lee/Life File (6 left, 111, 112, middle 3, 114 middle, 115 top, 116 all, 117, 142 top right), Damian Lovegrove/Science Photo Library (59), MAFF (irradiation symbol 114, 140), Dr P Marazzi/Science Photo Library (71 right), Marks & Spencer (113 top, 159 top, 161), Peter Menzel/Science Photo Library (69 bottom), Steven Milburn/Pifco Ltd (121 top), David Montford/Photofusion (56 right), Prof. P Motta/Dept of Anatomy/University 'La Sapienza', Rome/Science Photo Library (87 left & right), National Medical Slide Bank (72, 85, 88, 90), Northern Ireland Electric (158, 161), Ruth Nossek (113 bottom, 132, 133, 134, 151 bottom, 159 bottom), Office of Fair Trading (138), Pam Bewley Publicity/Magimix (118 top, 120 top), Catherine Pouedras/Eurelios/Science Photo Library (84), Prima International Group (120 bottom 3), Safeway (132, 133, 160), Nicola Sutton/Life File (86), TDI Advertising (Belfast) Ltd (132), Dave Thompson/Life File (42, 49), Ulster Bank (157, 158 bottom, 159 middle, 161), Ulster Folk and Transport Museum (168), Vegetarian Society (141).

Cover design by Lynda King
Page design by Jenny Fleet

The authors would like to thank Barbara Semple, Assistant Advisory Officer, NEELB, Glynis Henderson, Assistant Principal Moderator, CCEA, Pete Keogh, all the editors at Hodder & Stoughton, not least Ruth Nossek, and our respective families for their support and patience throughout this project.

Orders: please contact Bookpoint Ltd, 130 Milton Park, Abingdon, Oxon OX14 4SB. Telephone: (44) 01235 827720, Fax: (44) 01235 400454. Lines are open from 9.00 – 5.00, Monday to Saturday, with a 24 hour message answering service.

You can also order through our website www.hodderheadline.co.uk
A catalogue record for this title is available from the British Library

ISBN-10: 0 340 720670
ISBN-13: 978 0 340 72067 7
First published 1998
Impression number   10   9   8   7
Year   2007

Typeset by Wearset, Boldon, Tyne and Wear.
Printed in Dubai for Hodder Education a division of Hodder Headline, Ltd, 338 Euston Road, London NW1 3BH.

Foreword

This book is designed to meet the requirements of the Northern Ireland Programme of Study for KS4, including GCSE Home economics. The book is divided into three sections. These are the key areas of the syllabus:

- Family life
- Diet and health
- Choice and management of resources.

Each section is subdivided into chapters. The chapters address the syllabus content and process. Teacher delivery will enhance and strengthen pupil competence within the subject area by exploring issues used within the text to reflect practical and theoretical experiences provided.

The information is flexible enough to be used with all levels of ability. Every effort has been made to reflect the language used in the Programme of Study.

At the end of each chapter, key words are identified and there is a short summary of chapter content.

Questions provided are graded on a progression level to suit a range of abilities and are designed to assess pupil knowledge, application of information and evaluation of situations.

Information has been presented using different techniques, e.g. graphs, illustrations, diagrams, photographs, text, colour, etc. to sustain interest and to stimulate learning, acknowledging the fact that individuals learn in different ways. It is intended to be user friendly (teacher and pupil) with appropriate use of language, reinforcement of new terms using key words, effective presentation and extension work.

The appendices contain:

- a coursework model showing application of the process and giving sample coursework titles
- addresses of agencies for help and support for the family
- glossary of words used in coursework and examination papers.

The appendices are intended to be used in conjunction with the book content.

The text uses the language and approach intended for CCEA and aims to reflect CCEA examination styles.

Contents

SECTION 1
Family life

CHAPTER 1

Family roles and responsibilities

Definition of 'family'

Most people live in a family and the family is a very important influence in our lives. We all have our own ideas about what we mean by a family.

Generally, we accept that a family is a group of people who are related, either through birth, marriage or adoption, and who live together and give each other love and support.

Nuclear family

A **nuclear family** consists of parents and their child/children who live together. It is an independent group which manages its own affairs, with little or no help/support from grandparents or relations.

Extended family

An **extended family** is made up of a large family group which includes grandparents, parents, brothers, sisters, aunts, uncles, cousins and other relations who tend to live in the same area or nearby. Members of the family group help and support each other in times of need.

Lone/single parent family

A **lone parent family** is one where children are brought up by one parent only. This may be due to the divorce or separation of parents, a mother being unmarried and not living with the father, the death of one parent, or separation because of long-term imprisonment, working abroad, or lengthy hospitalization.

Lone/single parents have to take on the role of both parents, and this can be difficult, sometimes leading to financial or emotional problems.

Assistance may be available from the Department of Social Security (DSS).

Step-family

A **step-family** is one where the child or children are related to only one parent. The step-parent will take on a parenting role.

Reconstituted family

In a **reconstituted family** the parents have been married before and have joined together in a new relationship, bringing with them some or all of their children from a previous marriage.

Dual-earner family

A **dual-earner family** is one where both parents are in employment. The parents may need to make childcare provision.

Both parents may have decided to work to increase or supplement their income or perhaps so that they can each be financially independent. Many women also have careers and wish to continue to work when they have children.

Family with a disabled member

This is a family which has one member with a disability.

The disability may be mental or physical. It may be the result of an accident, disease, or illness or be congenital (born with it). The disabled person will need special care. Some disabilities mean extra work and expense for a family.

Foster family

A **foster family** is one which cares for children who cannot be cared for in their own home. Fostering is temporary, but can be long term or short term.

It is preferable to place children with a family, rather than in a residential home. The foster parents may be paid an allowance for the care of the child. Social services monitor the situation. The child can be returned to his/her own family once the problems have been resolved. If an arrangement is not suitable for any reason, the child can be moved to a different foster home.

Adoptive family

Adoption is a legal process whereby a couple undertake the parental responsibilities of caring for a child as if he/she were their own.

The child is given the adoptive parents' surname and his/her first name may also be changed. Children must be at least six weeks old before adoption is permitted. There is a probationary period of 13 weeks before the adoption is final in case the biological mother changes her mind. After this time, the biological parents have no legal rights or responsibilities.

Roles and responsibilities

Within a family there is a network of **roles** and **responsibilities**.

Each member of the family has a particular role, depending on his or her position in the family – father, mother, child, eldest, youngest, etc.

Roles within the family

Certain behaviour is expected of each family member. This is his/her role within the family. Each role carries certain responsibilities and family members come to expect these qualities of one another related to their roles.

Today, the role of the parent is not always clearly defined.

Since the Industrial Revolution almost 200 years ago, it has been the role of the father to go out to work and to be the 'bread winner'. Caring for children and running the home was the mother's role.

In the 20th century many things have happened to bring about changes in the role of the parent. For example:
- more and more women go out to work
- childcare provision and facilities are improving.

Both parents tend to share the responsibilities of running the home and caring for their children.

In a lone parent family one adult is responsible for everything, bringing in money, running the home and looking after the children, without the support of a partner.

> ### MORE ABOUT ROLES
>
> As you have already discovered, a role is the part you play in your family life. Family life is the most comfortable when each person has a role and is happy with it. Are the members of your family happy with the roles they have?

Role reversal

Role reversal takes place when, for example, the father cares for the home and the children, while the mother earns the money to provide for the family.

Shared roles

In some families, usually where both parents are working, household jobs and care of the children tend to be shared.

Responsibilities

To be a member of a family gives each person certain rights, as well as responsibilities.

Each member of the family, including the parent, has **physical**, **emotional**, **intellectual** and **social** needs which have to be met. It is the responsibility of parents to provide for the needs of their children.

PHYSICAL NEEDS	EMOTIONAL NEEDS
clothing	love
shelter	comfort
food	understanding
reproduction	security
finance	discipline
protection/safety	companionship
health care	stability
hygiene	affection
sleep	

INTELLECTUAL NEEDS	SOCIAL NEEDS
education	friends
stimulation	behaviour
moral values	independence
spiritual beliefs	social training
	communication

KEY WORDS

adoptive family
disabled member
dual-earner family
emotional
extended family
foster family
intellectual
lone parent family
nuclear family
physical
reconstituted family
responsibilities
role
role reversal
shared role
social
step-family

SUMMARY

- There are many types of family groups: nuclear, extended, lone parent, etc.
- Members of the family have a variety of roles. As society has changed, roles have become interchangeable.
- It is the responsibility of parents to provide a stable home for their children.
- Parents have needs as well as children.

QUESTIONS

1 Your role in the family is important to you. Describe your role, explaining your obligations.

2 Collect pictures to illustrate parents providing: (a) physical needs; (b) emotional needs; (c) intellectual needs; and (d) social needs.

3 Imagine you are a parent. Make up five rules which would make for a happy family.

4 What is the difference between 'shared roles' and 'role reversal'?

Changes in family life in the 20th century

In Chapter 1 we looked at the family and its responsibilities. Twentieth-century life has brought about many alternative family groups and as a result traditional methods of bringing up children have had to alter to suit the nature of each individual family.

The changing family group

Over 17 percent of today's households are headed by a lone parent. More than 1 in 6 families are now headed by lone mothers. Bringing up children without a partner has many implications for family life. Lone parent families are more likely than families with two parents to:

- be financially insecure
- live in substandard/poor housing conditions
- be in poor health
- receive care and help from the DSS.

This graph shows the number of mums and dads on family credit in 1990 compared with those on family credit in 1993, 1994, 1995 and 1996.

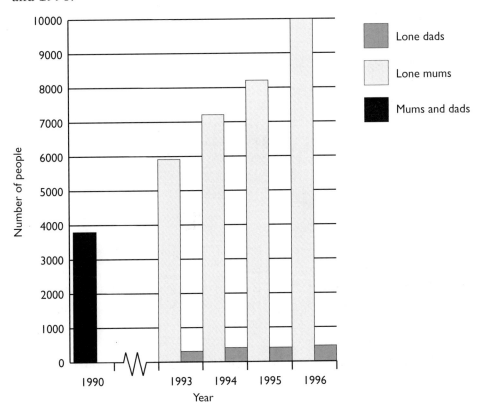

9

Being a lone parent is very hard work as the parent must shoulder all the responsibilities normally shared between two parents. The lone parent has to:

- be both a mother and a father figure
- run the home
- manage all money affairs
- provide for the children, both physically and emotionally
- be the disciplinarian
- seek employment to provide the money
- deal with problems as they arise
- carry the burden alone.

There may be benefits to being a one parent family. A lone parent family may be preferable to a family where there is violence or no love.

The low income trap

Lone parent families tend to be **low income** for many reasons, one of the main ones being that the majority of lone parents are women:

- women are more likely than men to have low-paid jobs
- lone parents can only work limited hours
- work must be convenient to home and childcare must be provided for.

Poor living conditions

Poor health

Poor housing can lead to ill-health, especially in young children, e.g. asthma, poor diet, underweight, overweight, malnourished, chest problems, frequent colds, low immunity.

Benefits

Families on a low income may qualify for benefits from the DSS, e.g. family credit, income support, social fund payments, etc.

> ### BENEFITS FOR LOW INCOME FAMILIES
>
> This is a tax free, weekly cash payment on top of Child Benefit for any single parent (whether divorced, separated or unmarried), regardless of income or National Insurance contributions. It is paid for one child only, usually the first.

Where a lone parent experiences difficulties or problems, help and advice can be obtained from the social services.

The dual-earner family

In many families both parents contribute to the family finances. The benefits of both parents working are:

● an improved standard of living
● a supplement to the existing income where one salary may not be enough
● provision of extra money for luxuries, e.g. holidays
● independence for each adult
● self-fulfilment for each adult
● both adults are able to socialize with peers
● provides a relief from boredom, loneliness or isolation.

Having two wages does not make life free from problems. The fact that both parents go out to work means that provision has to be made for the children and the usual household duties have to be carried out in the evenings or at weekends.

Problems facing dual-earning families

● childcare difficulties
● parents may leave home early and return late
● may have to bring work home
● household chores have to be completed in the evening or at weekends
● parents have to cope with children's homework, etc. in the evenings
● expense of childcare
● many household tasks tend to fall on the shoulders of the mother leaving her with a double workload
● little time to socialize
● parent may be mentally and physically exhausted
● childminder and parents may have different standards of discipline and childrearing ideas
● children may miss out on parental contact
● feelings of guilt.

Childcare options

Relatives

Advantages
- familiar with children
- may have similar standards
- more flexible for arrangements
- genuine love and affection
- trustworthy
- may come into the home.

Disadvantages
- may over-indulge child
- may be difficult for parents to give advice on childrearing to, for example, their own parents.

Day nurseries

A **day nursery** may be privately run, attached to the workplace or provided by the local authority.

Advantages
- qualified staff
- well equipped
- monitored for health and safety
- provide structured activities
- provide for pre-school and school children
- children mix with others
- good for social development
- insured
- give a daily report.

Disadvantages
- cannot care for sick children
- only work certain hours
- expensive
- child has to be taken out of home
- parents may need to provide nappies, food, etc.
- children may find it hard to settle.

Crèche

A **crèche** provides similar care to that provided by a day nursery but it is usually attached to the workplace. It can also be found in shopping centres, leisure centres, churches, etc.

Advantages
- parents can be close at hand
- staff are qualified
- hours suit workers
- well equipped.

Disadvantages
- cannot care for sick children
- may be expensive
- parents may have to provide food.

Childminder

A **childminder** is a person, usually a woman, who provides a childcare service in her own home. Childminders take only a few children and must be registered by the local authority.

Advantages

- parents choose the adult to care for their child
- being registered gives a sign of approval
- parents feel secure knowing their child is well looked after
- child mixes with other children
- will suit working hours of parents
- will take children after school/at holiday time
- may have a wider range of play equipment than own home
- may accommodate a sick child.

Disadvantages

- expensive
- parents may have to provide food and nappies
- child could pick up bad habits from other children
- may charge extra for anti-social hours
- may not have the same ideas on childrearing as parents.

Nanny

A **nanny** is a childminder who usually lives in the child's home.

Advantages

- available at short notice
- sole attention paid to child
- parents can dictate their own rules
- may have qualifications
- fits into child's routine
- develops a close bond as she lives with the family
- may help with housework.

Disadvantages

- needs accommodation
- lack of privacy for parents
- expensive.

Au pair

An **au pair** is, usually, a foreigner who provides some childcare services in exchange for board, accommodation and perhaps some pocket money.

Advantages

- cheap
- available at short notice
- fits into the child's routine
- develops a close bond with the family
- may help with the housework
- parents can dictate their own rules.

Disadvantages

- needs accommodation
- lack of privacy for parents
- language barrier
- usually young and may need discipline/help carrying out tasks
- not usually qualified.

Family with a disabled member

Nowadays, families with a **disabled** member are encouraged to care for this person in their own home and are given support to help them cope. The wider community is now more conscious of disabilities and is encouraged to make provision for disabled people. Children of school age may be integrated into mainstream schooling and can lead lives similar to able-bodied children, with the same opportunities and experiences.

Implications for the family of having a disabled member

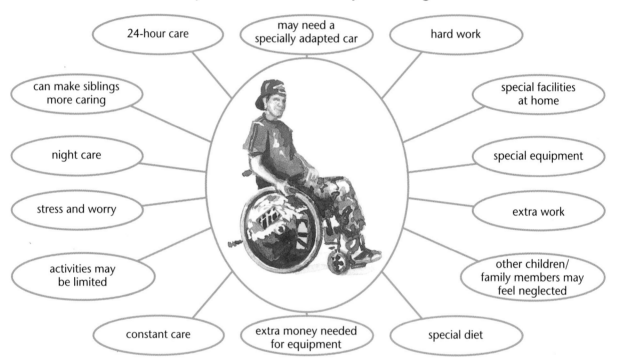

Caring for disabled people may be demanding. Other members of the family may not feel neglected if they have been involved in caring for their relative. Children involved in the care of a disabled sibling may grow up to be very responsible and selfless human beings. Caring for a disabled person is hard work and can last a lifetime, but there are sources of help for the carers.

HELP FOR FAMILIES FROM THE DSS

- severe disablement allowance
- attendance allowance for people aged 65 and over who need personal care
- disability living allowance for people under 65
- income support and housing benefit may be increased if a disabled person is living at home
- disability working allowance

OTHER PROVISION

- special schools
- day centres
- adult centres
- Physically Handicapped and Able-bodied (PHAB) Club
- Gateway Club
- respite care centres
- residential homes
- special holiday centres (SHARE)
- riding for the disabled

SUMMARY

- Family life has changed during the 20th century.
- A large percentage of families are headed by lone parents.
- Most lone parents are mothers.
- Lone parents have many difficulties in rearing their children alone.
- Many families have both parents working.
- Dual-earning families have advantages and disadvantages.
- Parents have many childcare options.
- Families are encouraged to care for a disabled member themselves.
- External support is available.

KEY WORDS

au pair
childcare
childminder
crèche
day nursery
disabled
low income
nanny

QUESTIONS

1 Analyse the graph on page 9 and give four reasons why there is such an increase in the number of lone parents.

2 State and explain three problems which may arise specifically for lone parent families.

3 Suggest why more mothers go out to work nowadays.

4 A young working mother with three small children aged two, three and five needs her children to be cared for while she is at work. Discuss options available to her and select the most suitable.

Family life cycle

Between birth and death a person goes through a series of stages. This growing-up process is called the **life cycle**.

The transition between some of these stages can often be stressful, for example during adolescence. Problems may occur at any stage of the life cycle and part of the family's job is to learn how to cope with these problems.

There are six stages in the life cycle.

Families are in a constant state of change as the members grow older and become more or less dependent on each other.

Whilst there are six stages in the life cycle, the person is only dependent on others during four or five: baby, toddler, child, adolescent and perhaps elderly. The level of dependency becomes less as the person grows. Eventually, the person becomes fully **independent**, and perhaps may have **dependants** of their own.

The family has certain **functions**. These functions can be grouped as follows:

- emotional .....   the development of healthy relationships
- economic .....   providing financial support
- protective .....   giving support to all the family
- reproductive .....   having children
- cultural/social .....   the socialization of the young
- intellectual/educational .....   providing a stimulating environment.

SUMMARY

- There are six stages in the life cycle.
- Family members require various types and levels of support at different stages of the life cycle.
- The family as a unit is responsible for many functions.

QUESTIONS

1 Name the six stages in the life cycle.

2 Which stage of the life cycle demands complete dependency on caring adults? Give reasons.

3 List four ways a baby is dependent on his/her parents.

4 Discuss ways a family provides a suitable environment to stimulate their children intellectually.

KEY WORDS
dependants
function
independent
life cycle

CHAPTER 4

Family relationships and needs

Family relationships are described as 'primary' relationships because the people involved generally know each other very well. Their ways of relating to each other are informal and intimate and should provide a close, loving relationship. There is a strong sense of belonging, identity and warmth. Within a family there is a network of relationships.

Primary relationships are formed:
● between parents
● between parents and children
● between siblings
● with other relatives
● with special friends.

The bond created through these relationships is essential to make each member of the family feel stable and secure throughout their life.

The needs of an individual can be categorized into four areas.

As a person progresses through the stages of the life cycle, their needs change. The table opposite illustrates some of these needs.

PHYSICAL

SOCIAL

EMOTIONAL

INTELLECTUAL

Family needs throughout the life cycle

	BABY / TODDLER	PRIMARY SCHOOL CHILD	ADOLESCENT	YOUNG ADULT	ADULT	ELDERLY
Physical	sleep food clothing shelter warmth health care hygiene safety body control voice control	sleep food clothing shelter warmth health care hygiene safety body control exercise	sleep food energy clothing shelter health care increased hygiene exercise increased nutrients	sleep food clothing shelter health care hygiene exercise	sleep food clothing shelter health care hygiene exercise rest and relaxation body care	sleep less food clothing shelter special health care hygiene less exercise more warmth
Social	contact with people communication family routine good habits	contact with others mix with other children communication routine social and behaviour training independence	friends independence communication family example confidence mobility	friends independence mix with others	family friends relaxation social interaction	family friends contact with people
Emotional	love affection bonding environment sense of belonging control of feelings discipline	love affection control of feelings discipline attitudes values sense of belonging	understanding love support values attitudes learning to develop own independence confidence respect responsibility develop coping qualities	love affection support independence stable relationships confidence responsibility	stable relationships privacy feeling valued respect love affection commitment security	cope with bereavement love feel needed feel useful self-respect respect self-confidence
Intellectual	creative and expressive play language development nursery education communication sense of danger	communication numbers science reading writing comprehension	general education money management realization of potential development of knowledge	career development development of knowledge development of potential	career development development of knowledge	keep mind active share experiences and knowledge cope with limitations

Commitment to relationships

People are social beings, having a strong need for interaction with others. To achieve this, they form groups of various kinds, e.g. a gang, friends, clubs, societies and the family.

Within these groups, relationships and bonds are formed. Bonds of love, affection and personal obligation are an integral part of a healthy social structure.

The family lays the foundation for all social relationships in and outside the home. Our closest relationships are likely to be with our family and some special friends, these are called **primary relationships**.

Relationships with our family are longstanding and essential in shaping our characters, values and attitudes.

They provide individuals with affection, security, guidance and a sense of belonging, which helps them to live in and relate to their wider environment and to the people within it.

Children who are brought up in this loving environment grow into well-adjusted, stable adults.

Good relationships require **commitment** from those involved, especially within marriage. A strong husband/wife relationship is of the utmost importance. Without this strength, it can destabilize the family as a unit.

Love and security

Children are dependent on their parents to fulfil their emotional needs of **love** and **security**. Parents should develop a warm, affectionate relationship with their children. The child that feels loved and wanted will develop a good self-image and will be able to form good relationships with others.

If a child lives with criticism,
  He learns to condemn,
If a child lives with hostility,
  He learns to fight,
If a child lives with ridicule,
  He learns to be shy,
If a child lives with shame,
  He learns to feel guilty,
If a child lives with tolerance,
  He learns to be patient,
If a child lives with encouragement,
  He learns confidence,
If a child lives with praise,
  He learns to appreciate,
If a child lives with fairness,
  He learns justice,
If a child lives with security,
  He learns to have faith,
If a child lives with approval,
  He learns to like himself,
If a child lives with acceptance and friendship,
  He learns to find love in the world.
                    Dorothy Law Holte

Respect

Respect means being able to appreciate and accept other people's views. Where parents show respect and tolerance towards each other, they set a good example for their children, and create a happy, harmonious environment. Children, in turn, will feel secure and grow up to be healthy, happy adults, who are self-confident and respectful of others.

Mutual support

Positive relationships are based on **mutual support** within the family. This means that everyone has a role to play in helping each other.

Family relationships are stronger when the members know that they can rely on each other.

Communication

A relationship cannot thrive without effective **communication**. Personal relationships are established and nurtured by verbal and non-verbal communication. Sulking, slamming doors and refusing to speak are all forms of non-verbal communication, but they do little to solve a problem. A conflict in a relationship is best solved by negotiation and calm discussion. Keeping the lines of communication open is the key to ending conflict and keeping a relationship alive.

It is important to develop communication skills throughout the different stages of the life cycle.

KEY WORDS

commitment
communication
love
mutual support
primary relationships
respect
security

SUMMARY

- The family lays the foundation for all social relationships.
- An individual has physical, social, emotional and intellectual needs. Many of these can be provided within the family.
- People need love and security.
- Respect means being able to appreciate and accept others.
- Effective communication is an important part of family life.

QUESTIONS

1 Describe the relationship you have with your family. Use these words to help you:

close	relaxed	respect	sharing
communicative	compromise	caring	dutiful
helpful	protective	loving	discussion
responsible	rights	respectful	

2 You have had a row with your mother. In what ways would you communicate your feelings of anger? How could this situation be resolved?

3 Discuss the ways adults might improve their relationship with adolescents?

4 Select one stage in the life cycle and make a spider diagram to illustrate the four areas of need.

The baby/toddler (0–3 months)

Physical development

All children grow and develop at their own rate. However, the order in which they learn to do things generally follows similar patterns. These are commonly known as **milestones** of development.

The pictures below illustrate some of these stages.

AT BIRTH
- needs total support
- has no body control

3 MONTHS
- turns head to sound
- still needs some support
- can hold head steady

6 MONTHS
- develops hand skills
- can sit upright with support

9 MONTHS
- can sit unsupported
- can turn to either side
- may be able to pull to sit or stand without help

12 MONTHS/1 YEAR
- stands
- walks with support
- may crawl or move around on bottom
- can pick up toys

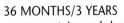

36 MONTHS/3 YEARS
- goes upstairs and down one foot at a time
- may jump off step
- can ride tricycle
- may try to dress without help

23

Feeding the baby

BREAST MILK	BOTTLE MILK
• contains all the correct nutrients for the baby • contains antibodies to protect the baby from illness • is at the correct temperature • costs nothing • is easy for the baby to digest • is clean and safe • helps to create a bond between mother and baby • baby can be fed anywhere	• it is easy to see how much the baby is taking • the baby can be fed anywhere • any adult can feed the baby • the father can feed the baby and develop a close bond • the mother can get more rest • the mother can return more easily to work • bottles can be made in advance and stored safely in a refrigerator

Weaning

Weaning describes the process of moving the baby on from breast or bottle milk to solid foods. It is usually recommended that weaning begin around four months. The danger of weaning before four months is that the baby may become overweight, develop food allergies or suffer from indigestion. Weaning too early may cause kidney damage.

Weaning introduces babies to different tastes and textures. A variety of foods should be introduced slowly:
• to meet the changing nutritional needs of the growing baby
• to encourage the transition from a liquid diet to family foods.

Whilst home-prepared foods may be the ideal choice, tins, jars and packets of baby food can be very useful, as they are quick, convenient and easy to prepare when only small quantities are required.

Care of the baby/toddler

Before birth, a baby is protected and sheltered in the mother's womb, but once born, a new development stage begins.

The baby has to adjust to a new and different environment. Babies can do some things alone, without any help, e.g. breathing, but in other ways they are completely helpless and therefore dependent on an adult.

Good **hygiene** is important to maintain good health and prevent disease.

Bathing

A baby should be kept clean.

1 Ensure that the room is warm (20°C) and draught free.
2 Collect all the bath items (towels, clean clothes, clean nappy, cotton wool, changing mat).
3 Check water. Always put cold water into the bath first.
4 Wrap the undressed baby in a warm towel, leaving nappy on.
5 Gently clean the baby's face and head with dampened cotton wool.

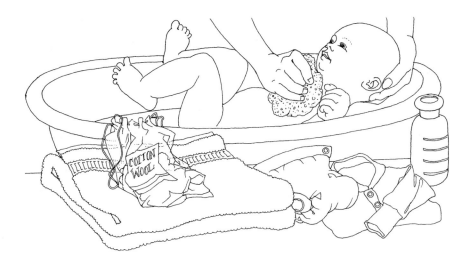

6 Remove the nappy and place the baby into the bath, supporting both back and head.
7 Wash the baby's body and then lift out onto a towel.
8 Dry the baby gently, paying special attention to the baby's creases.
9 Dress the baby in fresh, warm clothing.

Changing a nappy

As the baby becomes more independent, encourage good hygiene habits.

1 Collect all the necessary items (nappy, cotton wool, water, changing mat).
2 Lay the baby on a flat surface using a changing mat.
3 Remove the soiled nappy and wash the baby's bottom, paying special attention to creases.

4 Dry the bottom and use a nappy cream, if necessary.
5 Put a fresh nappy on the baby.

Immunization

Children are **immunized** (vaccinated) against certain diseases in order to protect them from catching or developing them. A special vaccine is required for each disease.

Here is a sample immunization schedule.

AGE DUE	IMMUNIZATION
2 months	1st Diphtheria, Tetanus, Whooping Cough, Polio, Hib
3 months	2nd Diphtheria, Tetanus, Whooping Cough, Polio, Hib
4 months	3rd Diphtheria, Tetanus, Whooping Cough, Polio, Hib
15 months	Measles, Mumps, Rubella (MMR)
4–5 years	Booster Diphtheria, Tetanus, Polio and MMR

Teething

The first set of teeth are called milk teeth. There are 20 in total.
1 Clean teeth with a good toothbrush and toothpaste.
2 Keep sugary foods to a minimum.
3 Do not dip a dummy in honey or sugar.
4 Avoid sugary drinks after teeth have been cleaned at bedtime.

5 Visit the dentist regularly to familiarize the child with the dentist and to have teeth checked.
6 Encourage children to eat fresh fruit and vegetables rather than sugary foods.

Safety

A baby's natural curiosity may put him/her in danger. It is the parent's responsibility to train the baby to take care of him/herself and to help him/her to become independent.

Very young children require supervision for their own **safety**.

Inside the home

- keep medicines and poisonous substances out of reach
- use a safety gate on stairs and doorways
- use fire and cooker guards
- cover electrical sockets
- keep sharp objects out of reach
- put safety locks on windows and cupboards
- keep plastic bags out of reach
- store matches and lighters out of reach.

Outside the home

- keep all garden tools and chemicals locked up
- cover or fence off ponds and areas of water
- keep gate securely closed
- remove poisonous plants
- beware of dog's and cat's excrement
- keep fences in good repair
- check for broken glass
- keep garden toys in good condition.

Cars

- use an approved infant carrier for young baby, secured by seat belt
- use child locks on rear doors
- strap or harness all children securely
- use an appropriate child seat up to the age of four
- do not leave children unattended in the car.

KEY WORDS

bottle milk
breast milk
hygiene
immunization
milestones
safety
weaning

SUMMARY

- Milestones of development provide rough guidelines to the things that the average child can do at certain stages of development.
- Babies can be breast or bottle fed.
- Weaning describes the process of moving the baby from a diet of milk to one comprising a variety of solid foods.
- Personal hygiene and care of the teeth are important for the health of the child.
- Immunization protects the child against certain diseases.
- Safety is important, both inside and outside the home.

QUESTIONS

1 What is meant by 'milestones of development'?

2 Describe the physical changes that take place in a baby between birth and the age of 12 months.

3 Why is it unwise to begin weaning before the age of around four months?

4 Make a flow chart showing the correct bathtime routine for a baby. Illustrate your chart.

5 Make a list of 'do's and don'ts' for the care of teeth.

6 Look at the picture below and make a list of the dangers for a toddler that you can see.

7 Research which day the baby clinic is held in your health centre and what checks are carried out there.

CHAPTER 6

The primary school child (4–11 years)

Physical development

A typical four year old has boundless energy and a natural curiosity. Up to this stage in his/her life his/her growth rate has been quite rapid and the average four year old will be approximately 92–101 cm tall and weigh 15–18 kg.

PHYSICAL SKILLS

gross motor skills
- runs
- jumps
- skips
- climbs ladders
- swings
- rides a bicycle with stabilizers
- hops on one foot
- can kick and throw a ball

fine motor skills
- uses paints, crayons to make pictures
- holds a pencil
- writes

SOCIAL SKILLS
- can go to the toilet alone
- washes own hands
- ties shoe laces
- eats with a knife and fork
- dresses and undresses
- converses with another person
- beginning to share

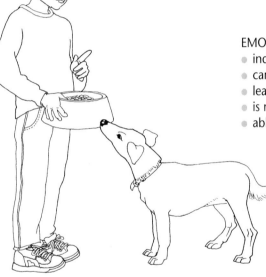

EMOTIONAL SKILLS
- independent
- can comfort friends when they are upset
- learning to control their feelings
- is responsive to discipline
- able to protect and care for younger children and pets

INTELLECTUAL SKILLS
- speaks fluently in understandable sentences
- listens to and can tell stories
- has a good imagination
- can recognize letters of the alphabet
- has some concept of time
- always asking questions: How? Who? What? Where? Why? When?
- knows own name, home address and age

Starting school

Children are legally required to attend school from the age of four years. At this stage, children have to learn to be independent as they are leaving familiar surroundings to enter a new and strange environment.

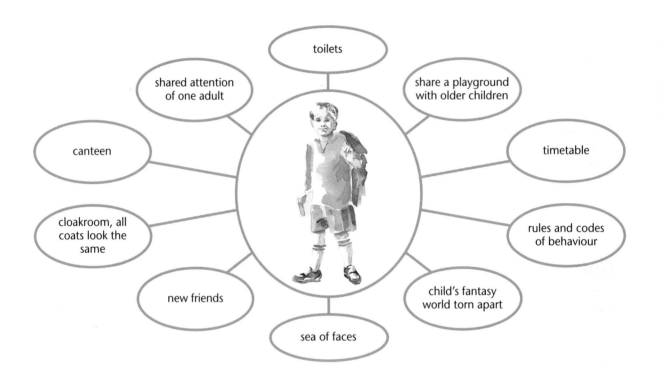

HOW PARENTS CAN HELP

- show plenty of love and understanding
- encourage the child and show an interest in books and learning – motivate
- talk to the child about school
- buy all the equipment and uniform the child needs for school
- encourage the child to take part in all activities in school
- enrol in a playgroup/school the year before school begins
- show interest and enthusiasm
- hide any negative emotions from the child

HOW SCHOOL CAN HELP

- arrange a pre-school visit during the summer term before starting school
- introduce the teacher and some of the peer group to the child
- show the child his/her classroom
- explain the school day routine
- provide parental help

Sibling rivalry

At this turning point in his/her life, the young school child may also be faced with the arrival of a new baby brother or sister. No matter how much love a young child is given, a certain amount of jealousy is inevitable.

This is called **sibling rivalry** and can manifest itself in behavioural changes, e.g. temper tantrums, bedwetting, regression, baby talk, clinging to mother, thumbsucking, refusal to eat. Should this negative behaviour occur, the child will need a lot of reassurance and attention to prevent any feelings of being left out.

WAYS PARENTS CAN HELP

- prepare the child for the new arrival and the separation from the mother
- involve the child in the baby's routine, e.g. bathtime
- allow time to be with the older child alone
- reassure the child that he/she is loved and wanted
- encourage the child to be independent
- avoid comparisons with the new baby

Food for the primary school child

Food for children should be highly nutritious and attractively presented in small, easy-to-manage helpings.

As children are growing rapidly they need a good supply of nutrients: calcium, protein, carbohydrate, minerals, vitamins and fibre to ensure proper growth and development.

NUTRIENTS	SOURCES	FUNCTIONS
Calcium	milk and dairy produce, yoghurts	bones and teeth
Protein	meat, fish, eggs, milk, pulses and cheese	growth and repair of cells
Carbohydrate	pasta, breads, potatoes, cereals	energy and warmth
Vitamins and minerals	fruit and vegetables	general good health
Fibre	cereals, fruit and vegetables, wholegrain foods	healthy bowel movements

Children should be encouraged to avoid:
- eating between meals
- faddy habits
- sweet, sugary food and drinks
- over-processed foods
- fried and salted foods.

Safety

A child of primary school age still needs adult supervision at all times. Statistics show that the number of road accidents involving young children increases when children start school. It is important to train the child in good road safety practices:

- know the Green Cross Code
- wear a seat belt while in the car
- use safety helmets when cycling
- wear fluorescent bands/clothing and reflectors which are visible in poor light.

It is a parent's responsibility to ensure that the home and its environment is safe and secure for the growing child.

KEY WORDS

emotional
intellectual
nutrients
physical
sibling rivalry
social

SUMMARY

- At primary school age, children start to develop independent skills.
- Starting school is a major life event.
- Parents need to prepare children for starting school.
- A new baby can cause emotional distress for some children (sibling rivalry).
- Young children need a healthy, balanced diet.
- Parents should teach good safety practices.

QUESTIONS

1 Discuss what type of resources would improve a child's physical, social and intellectual skills.

2 Record your findings in a chart, or on computer spreadsheet.

3 Some four year olds experience problems when starting school. List some of these problems.

4 Describe how a child could be helped to settle into school life.

5 Suggest a suitable packed lunch for a primary school child. Give reasons for your choice.

The adolescent (12–17 years)

Adolescence is the period during which a child develops into an adult. During this time there are physical, emotional and mental changes which can be traumatic and confusing for the adolescent.

Physical development/puberty

Puberty brings physical changes, preparing, the child's body for adulthood and reproduction. The onset of puberty can vary depending on the individual. No two individuals are alike.

GIRLS	BOYS
growth spurt	growth spurt
usually between 12 and 15 years	usually between 13 and 16 years
pubic and under arm hair begin to grow	pubic, facial and under arm hair begin to grow
breast development	penis and testes increase in size
hips become more rounded	voice becomes deeper
menstruation (period) begins	shoulders become broader

All these changes may cause adolescents to feel self-conscious and awkward for a short time. Relationships with parents can change as friendships with other adolescents become more important. It is important for the adolescent to take regular exercise and to be more aware of personal hygiene at this time.

Social development

Social development begins early in childhood and continues during the adolescent years. During this time a child's personality is unfolding, giving him/her an identity of his/her own. Parental control and values play a large part in the formation of character. Environmental factors and friends also make a contribution.

Society demands that everyone, including adolescents, behave in an acceptable manner. This is the norm. Serious deviation from the norm can cause conflict with authorities such as police, school and parents, resulting in various forms of punishment – detention, being taken to court and imprisonment. However, it is not unusual for adolescents to experiment with ideas, behaviour or attitudes, which are considered to be rebellious.

When adolescents reject the rules laid down by parents, conflict results. Rigid attitudes by parents, denying the adolescent some level of independence, may lead to rebellion. Ideally, adolescents and parents need to compromise.

Emotional development

Emotions are our feelings. Emotional development is how we learn to cope with our feelings about ourselves and about others.

Good emotional development requires:
- positive self-image (sometimes called self-esteem)
- good family relationships (feeling wanted and loved)
- acceptance by others
- ability to cope with emotions such as love, fear and anger.

The adolescent begins to take an interest in the opposite sex. These feelings are usually based on a physical attraction. Such relationships are not usually long lasting or mature.

Intellectual development

Adolescence is a time of rapid intellectual development. Whilst we are all born with a certain level of ability, this can be enriched or hindered by:
- our environment (home, family, peers)
- level of motivation (parents, self, peers, school).

This is a time when the young person is preparing for major examinations. To succeed requires self-discipline at school and in the home and this can prove very challenging because of peer pressure and parental expectations. Decisions made at this time will affect the rest of his/her life.

Peer pressure

During adolescence, the young person tries to move away from total dependence on his/her parents to a certain degree of independence.

At this stage, the peer group replaces family support, supplying the feeling of togetherness and acceptance without criticism. **Peer pressure** can have both positive and negative effects.

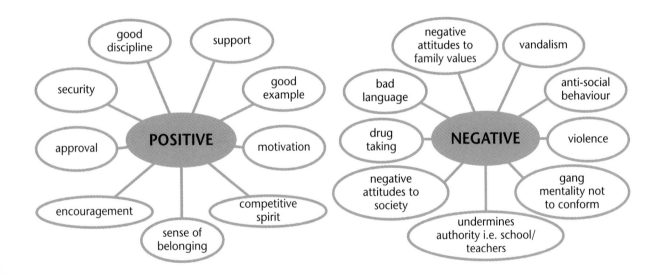

HOW PARENTS CAN HELP THEIR ADOLESCENT OFFSPRING

- try to be understanding
- give the adolescent some freedom and responsibilities
- let the adolescent make his/her own mistakes
- give advice when asked for it
- try not to be too critical
- include the adolescent in family discussions
- give the adolescent privacy
- talk freely about sexual problems

Food

As adolescents develop into young adults their metabolic rate changes, demanding greater quantities of energy foods.

It is wiser to choose from carbohydrate sources (e.g. pasta, potatoes and cereals) as fat sources, whilst high in energy, may lead to health disorders such as obesity, skin problems and heart disease.

At this stage, growth is rapid so a good supply of protein is required.

Growing involves bone formation so foods containing calcium and vitamin D are essential.

Adolescent girls need a good supply of iron to prevent anaemia and vitamin C for the absorption of iron.

Wholegrain foods, together with fresh fruit and vegetables, help prevent constipation.

At this stage, adolescents are very easily influenced in their eating patterns. Food habits may be changed by the influence of peers, the media (advertisements), fashion or fads, money and freedom of choice. This could lead to vegetarianism, irregular eating, preference for fast foods, etc. Adolescents need to ensure that their eating habits do not result in an unbalanced diet.

DO	DON'T
• eat regular meals	• eat too many foods high in sugar, fat and salt
• eat plenty of salads	
• eat a wide variety of foods	• snack
• drink water, pure fruit juice	• succumb to food 'fads'
• try new foods	• eat between meals
• use herbs instead of salt	

Possible health disorders

Adolescents are particularly susceptible to a number of health disorders:
• skin disorders
• obesity
• anorexia nervosa
• bulimia nervosa
• dental caries.

Leisure for adolescents

Adolescents can suffer from stress due to their emotional and physical development, and the conflicts they may experience at this time. Leisure pursuits can alleviate this stress and present the opportunity to 'let out their emotions', as well as providing an environment to meet other young people.

Leisure needs can be considered as social, physical, educational or personal, but will be dictated by or controlled as given in the following table.

	CONTROLLED BY	EXAMPLES
social	money available	youth clubs
physical	time available	sports clubs
educational	social and cultural background	sea cadets
personal	family background	scouts
		guides
		Red Cross
		Duke of Edinburgh award
		cinemas
		libraries
		discos

SUMMARY

- Adolescence is the transition period from childhood to adulthood.
- This stage can be difficult and stressful for parents and adolescents.
- Adolescents experience many physical and emotional changes.
- Peer pressure can affect adolescents in a positive or negative manner.
- Adolescents need to maintain healthy eating habits to ensure proper growth and to prevent dietary disorders.
- Adolescents find many ways to relax and unwind.

KEY WORDS

adolescence
growth spurt
peer pressure
puberty

QUESTIONS

1 You want to go to the local nightclub with your friends. Your parents are against you going because of nasty rumours about the nightclub. In groups discuss the problem. Record your (the adolescent's) viewpoint and the parents' viewpoint.
Role play the discussion between adolescent and parents for the rest of the class.

2 Describe three positive and three negative influences which peers can exert upon an adolescent.

3 An adolescent's daily diet consists of:

Breakfast	*Mars bar*
Break	*two packets of crisps and a diet coke*
Lunch	*curried chips*
Evening meal	*beef burger and a coke*

Evaluate the suitability and effects of a diet like this for a growing adolescent. Suggest alternatives.

4 Return to the situation set in Question 1 and suggest a strategy which you (the adolescent) and your parents could use to resolve the situation.

CHAPTER 8

The young adult (18–25 years)

Adulthood begins at the age of 18. This is the age when a person can vote, leave school to begin third level education, **leave home** without parental consent, take out a bank loan without a guarantor, give blood, get a passport, change name, is fully responsible for his/her own decisions, and generally gains his/her **independence**.

Reasons for leaving home

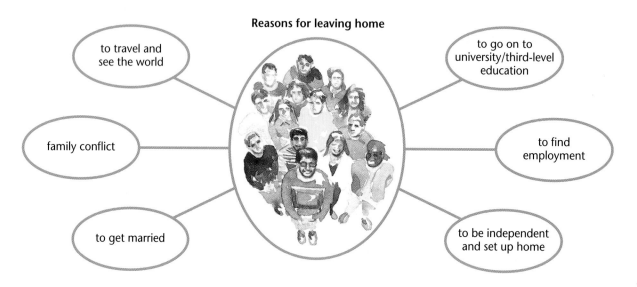

- to travel and see the world
- to go on to university/third-level education
- family conflict
- to find employment
- to get married
- to be independent and set up home

Implications of leaving home

There are some practical problems which need to be resolved when a person leaves home.

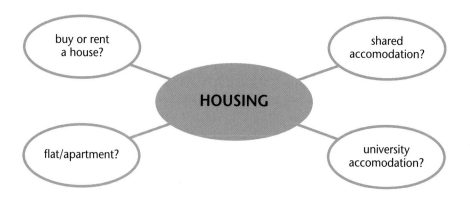

- buy or rent a house?
- shared accomodation?
- **HOUSING**
- flat/apartment?
- university accomodation?

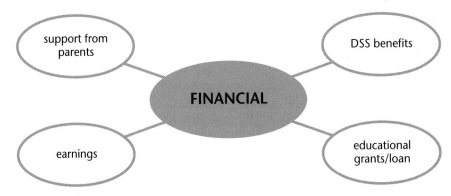

Adult relationships

Relationships do not remain static. They change as individuals grow and mature. At the age of 18, a young adult takes on new responsibilities similar to those of his/her parents. These similar experiences may bring him/her closer to his/her parents than he/she was during the adolescent years. It is not unusual for a young adult to take on a friendship role with his/her parents, being able to confide in them as well as give and take advice.

When a young person leaves home, this can cause a mixture of emotions. Leaving home is a major event and can be positive or negative for both parents and child.

EFFECTS OF LEAVING HOME	
Positive	**Negative**
● can bring parents and child closer	● separation can prevent resolving of differences
● total independence for young adult	● parents may feel a sense of loss
● gives a sense of responsibility	● young adult can feel homesick/lonely
● gives parents more financial freedom	● poverty and hardship
● gives young adult an appreciation of home comforts	● financial strain on parents
● creates opportunities to develop new relationships	

Needs of the young adult

PHYSICAL
- food
- shelter
- clothing
- hygiene
- exercise
- health care
- sleep

INTELLECTUAL
- career development
- development of knowledge
- development of potential

EMOTIONAL
- love
- affection
- support
- independence
- confidence
- responsibility
- stable relationships

SOCIAL
- friends
- independence
- mixing with others

Friendships

The young adult, once independent, may broaden his/her range of social relationships. People have a strong need to mix with others. **Friendships** occur with the people we meet in our day-to-day lives. These are generally brief acquaintances. However, people can become close and socially dependent on each other, so that bonds of trust, honesty and closeness are created. Relationships where there are strong bonds of love, affection and intimacy along with companionship usually form the basis for more long lasting, permanent, stable relationships such as marriage. Qualities which strengthen marital relationships include loyalty, trust, honesty and fidelity.

Starting work

Whilst many 16 year olds have part-time jobs, it is more usual to seek full-time **employment** at the age of 18. Embarking on full-time employment is a major turning point in the young adult's life. He/she requires less parental support and may contribute to the running costs of the home. He/she may become involved in making decisions and generally take on a more responsible role. These responsibilities may involve not only household chores but also the care of younger siblings. If parents rely too much on older children, or children are unwilling to help, this can become a source of conflict.

Unemployment

It is a fact of life that many young people cannot find permanent employment. There are a number of reasons, for example:

- lack of qualifications or training
- area in which he/she lives
- inability to work through illness or disability
- unwillingness to work
- new technology lessening job opportunities.

EFFECTS OF UNEMPLOYMENT

- lack of money/possible debts
- health may suffer
- stress
- depression/suicidal tendencies
- loss of self-esteem
- may turn to crime
- strain on relationships
- dependency on DSS
- social outcast
- undisciplined lifestyle
- negative attitudes
- loss of confidence

SUMMARY

- Young people leave home for many reasons.
- Independent life skills are developed when people leave home.
- Managing finance and shelter (housing) becomes a person's own responsibility.
- Relationships that are more stable may be developed.
- Starting full-time work is a major life event.
- Many young people remain unemployed.

KEY WORDS

employment
friendships
independence
leaving home
relationships
unemployment

QUESTIONS

1 John cannot find a job. How might this affect him?

2 Pamela is working away from home having spent 18 years living with her parents. Discuss ways in which her life will change. Record your conclusions.

3 Look at Question 2 again. List Pamela's new responsibilities.

4 Identify qualities needed for a permanent stable relationship. Justify your answer.

CHAPTER 9

The adult (26–64 years)

Many adults settle into a permanent **relationship** during their mid twenties and are ready for the commitment of family responsibilities.

The decision to become a parent involves the greatest personal **responsibility** that a person ever has to make. It is essential that both partners agree on the decision to have children as it is a life-long commitment.

Having children changes the lifestyle of a couple in the following ways:

● long-term responsibility (children normally stay at home until at least 16 years of age)
● raising children is expensive
● children require a great deal of time, therefore parents have less time for themselves or to socialize
● parental freedom is restricted
● a wide range of social, emotional, intellectual and physical needs must be catered for by the parents
● parents must set a satisfactory standard of values.

When a baby is born the relationship between the parents may change. They will no longer be able to devote so much time to one another. There will be more work and responsibilities, which need to be shared by both parents. If both parents are working, then household duties and childcare need to be fairly distributed to prevent conflict and disagreement. Communication is the best way to overcome any problems which may arise in this new role as parents.

Parental responsibilities

Parenting skills evolve gradually as the parent becomes more experienced and as the child's needs change. The responsibilities of the parent are based on a set of needs, essential for the child's physical, intellectual, social and emotional wellbeing.

The wellbeing of the child

The function of the family is to provide a caring, stable environment in which children can grow and develop.

GOOD PARENTING   POOR PARENTING

Physical

- comfortable home
- good food
- safe environment
- warmth

A

- neglected home
- dilapidated building
- dirty surroundings
- lack of nutritious food

B

Intellectual

- home with two-way communication
- plenty of stimulation
- entertainment
- toys/books, etc.

C

- absence of toys/books, etc.
- lack of attention
- no stimulation
- criticism

D

Emotional

- praise
- encouragement
- protection

- abuse
- neglect
- disregard

E

F

Social

- opportunities to play with others
- spending time together
- discipline

- lack of friends
- little parental interaction
- poor discipline

G

H

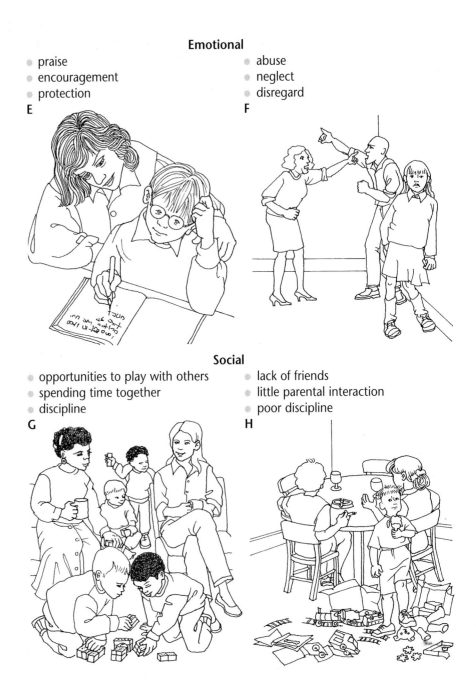

Attitudes and values

Children's **attitudes** and **values** are shaped by their parents and the people with whom they socialize. Parents are their first teachers and exert the greatest influence, especially in the early years. Parents can set a good or bad example by their attitude and behaviour towards their partner, their children and others.

For example, if parents are intolerant of each other, the children may also be intolerant of others. Children who are praised for helping in the home will feel valued and be encouraged to help more often.

ATTITUDES THAT MAY BE TRANSFERRED TO CHILDREN

Positive	Negative
● respect	● criticism
● praise	● condemnation
● tolerance	● hostility
● patience	● ridicule
● confidence	● intolerance
● appreciation	● guilt
● justice	● aggression
● fairness	● lack of respect
● approval	
● love	
● kindness	
● acceptance	

Discipline

It is necessary to **discipline** children so that they:
● are socially acceptable to those around them
● understand the difference between right and wrong
● are protected from danger
● learn self-control.

For discipline to be effective, children must be old enough to understand what is expected of them.

Discipline should be consistent, kind, reasonable and firm.

Parents may sometimes find enforcing discipline a difficult part of their role.

PARENTS SHOULD

● set a good example
● mean what they say
● avoid a situation they cannot win
● be consistent
● support each other's decisions
● be reasonable
● not have expectations that are too high
● reward good behaviour
● be able to admit when they have made a mistake and apologize

Lack of discipline or excessive discipline can also be harmful as it can make a child feel unwanted, unloved, insecure and fearful.

No child is perfect!

Fostering independence

All children should be encouraged to become independent. Independence develops gradually with practice and encouragement from parents. The move towards independence begins even before the child starts school, as soon as the child is able to understand and to control their motor skills. There are many ways in which parents can help foster independence. For example, the child should be trained/allowed to:

Before school
1 Tie his/her shoe laces.
2 Use a knife and fork.
3 Blow his/her nose.
4 Use the toilet without help.

Early primary school
1 Use the Green Cross Code.
2 Tidy up after him/herself.
3 Be responsible for his/her possessions.
4 Set the table.
5 Help with clearing up and washing the dishes.

Upper primary school
1 Do messages.
2 Be responsible for specific jobs around the house.
3 Bath him/herself/wash his/her own hair.
4 Walk to school.
5 Be able to care for a pet.

Secondary/Lower secondary school
1 Be responsible with pocket money.
2 Go to youth club/scouts, etc.
3 Stay up later.
4 Participate in some family decisions, e.g. holidays.
5 Visit friends. Stay overnight.
6 Have his/her own space, privacy.
7 Choose his/her own clothes.
8 Make subject choice at school.

Upper secondary school
1 Stay out late.
2 Go to discos.
3 Learn to drive.
4 Have boy/girl relationships.
5 Take part in family decisions.
6 Be self-sufficient in the home, e.g. cooking for him/herself.
7 Make his/her own decisions.
8 Follow current fashion trends.

Ideally, a child should be completely independent by the age of 18. During adolescence, teenagers may want more independence than parents are willing to give. This can cause conflict and lead to strained relationships.

Coping with adolescence

Some parents find it difficult to accept that their children are growing up.

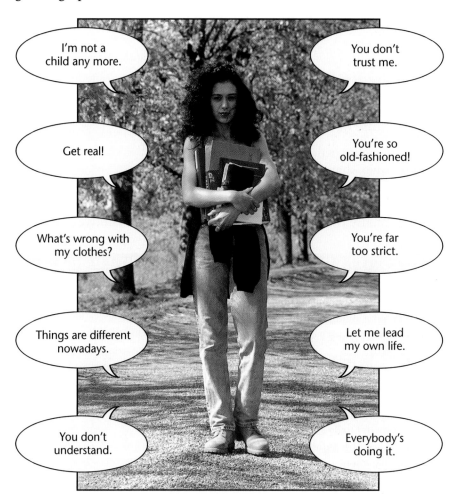

HOW DO PARENTS COPE?

- be understanding
- communicate
- be patient
- give them space
- be trusting
- try not to criticize
- give responsibility
- do not embarrass them
- let them make their own decisions
- let them make their own mistakes
- be fair and consistent
- be there for them and give support in times of need
- provide a loving, secure environment

Role reversal

Family life has changed a lot during the 20th century. The traditional role of the man was:

- to provide financial support for his family
- to be the disciplinarian
- to make all the major decisions.

The woman was responsible for:

- the care of the home
- the welfare of the children
- the welfare of her husband.

Roles have changed:

- sometimes shared
- sometimes reversed
- sometimes the sole responsibility of one parent
- occasionally the responsibility of children in the family.

FACTORS WHICH HAVE BROUGHT ABOUT CHANGE

- equal opportunities for women
- contraception, smaller families
- equal educational opportunities
- women are more independent and do not always feel the need to get married
- technological advances within the home, work and the environment
- divorce is easier
- provision is available for care of the elderly outside the home
- improved childcare provision
- increase in family breakdown
- increase in the number of lone parent families
- unemployment

Shared roles

Roles can also be **shared**. In this case both parents may be at home or in employment. They share household tasks and the care of the children as well as contributing to the family budget. Shared roles are beneficial, in that father, mother and children can become closer. There is mutual support between parents and an appreciation of home management. Couples who successfully share roles usually have a stronger and more stable relationship.

Role reversal

When **role reversal** occurs, the mother works outside the home to provide financial support for the family while the father remains at home to look after the children and the home. Unemployment is one of the main reasons for role reversal.

Roles taken on by a lone parent

The increase in the number of families that break down and of lone parent families means that the responsibilities and roles traditionally managed by two parents are sometimes taken on by one parent alone.

Roles taken on by children

Occasionally, for example when a parent becomes ill or is disabled, roles usually taken on by parents become the responsibility of the child.

Stereotyping

To **stereotype** people is to put them into strict groups and expect them all to behave in a certain, predictable way, ignoring their individual characteristics and abilities.

Here are some typical, stereotyping comments:

Boys are strong, girls are weak

All football fans are hooligans

All American tourists are loud

All nurses are female

All blondes are dumb

All unemployed people are lazy

All lorry drivers are men

Housework is for women

Men don't cry

51

Stereotyping often leads to people of different sexes, religions, colours and nationalities being unfairly treated and denied equal opportunities. This attitude is gradually changing. The law encourages equality to eliminate discrimination. Where it still exists, stress and conflict may result.

Family breakdown

If a couple's relationship becomes impossible, they may decide to live apart. This can be a traumatic experience for the couple and especially for any children. On the other hand, couples who decide to stay together for the sake of the children can do more harm than good. A stable, lone parent family may be a better option.

Separation may mean having to arrange alternative accommodation and independent sources of income.

The impact of the separation will be felt by the children because of:
- new living arrangements
- changing relationships
- having to adapt to a whole new environment.

EFFECTS OF FAMILY BREAKDOWN ON CHILDREN

- may be emotionally disturbed
- may feel insecure
- have divided loyalties
- may behave in an anti-social way
- may regress in development
- may feel responsible
- may behave badly at school
- may not reach their potential at school

Serious illness

When serious illness occurs in the home it has many implications for the family lifestyle and the division of roles and responsibilities. The person who is sick may be unable to carry out his/her normal daily tasks. He/she may need practical help and emotional support. Many may suffer great pain and discomfort, as well as psychological distress. He/she becomes the focus of attention and everyone else's needs become secondary. If the illness is long term or debilitating, the whole family will be affected and individual roles and responsibilities will change as it becomes necessary to meet the needs of the family member who is ill.

SUMMARY

- Adulthood is the time when people enter into permanent relationships.
- Commitment is necessary for a stable relationship and a stable home.
- Parenthood brings many responsibilities:
  - the wellbeing of children
  - encouraging sound attitudes and values
  - discipline
  - fostering independence
  - coping with adolescence.
- Stereotyping is a fixed way of looking at people and their roles.
- Changes in family life and employment have eliminated distinct male and female roles.

KEY WORDS

attitudes
discipline
parenting
relationship
responsibility
role reversal
shared roles
stereotype
values

● ●

QUESTIONS

1 What changes does parenthood bring to a couple's life?

2 List the physical needs (that parents must provide) of a newborn baby.

3 Observe the scenes in pictures C and D and discuss how important it is for parents to provide a stimulating environment for their children.

4 A toddler is having a temper tantrum in the supermarket. Suggest strategies which the parent could use to resolve the situation.

5 List six areas of conflict which may arise between parents and adolescents. Select three and suggest how parents and adolescent may compromise.

6 Explain the implications for the family if one parent becomes seriously ill.

The elderly (65+ years)

The elderly are defined as those who have reached a **retirement** age of 65 years and over.

On retirement, a person's lifestyle often changes dramatically. When no longer in paid employment they will have more time to fill, but possibly less money to spend. As they get even older, their health may deteriorate.

The needs of an elderly person take on a new dimension and are different from those of working adults.

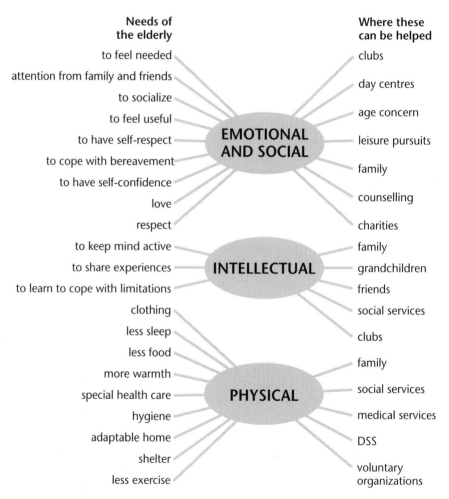

Needs of the elderly		Where these can be helped
to feel needed		clubs
attention from family and friends		day centres
to socialize		age concern
to feel useful	**EMOTIONAL AND SOCIAL**	leisure pursuits
to have self-respect		family
to cope with bereavement		counselling
to have self-confidence		
love		charities
respect		
to keep mind active		family
to share experiences	**INTELLECTUAL**	grandchildren
to learn to cope with limitations		friends
clothing		social services
less sleep		clubs
less food		family
more warmth		social services
special health care	**PHYSICAL**	medical services
hygiene		DSS
adaptable home		voluntary organizations
shelter		
less exercise		

Time

Once no longer in regular, paid employment, the elderly have more time to meet friends and to pursue other activities and interests. Some people find it difficult to adjust to a more leisurely lifestyle.

They may feel isolated from colleagues and may have problems using their time.

BENEFITS OF HAVING TIME
• can take advantage of 'off season' holidays
• can live in warmer climates during the winter
• can meet and make new friends
• can learn new skills
• can pursue hobbies they did not have time for when at work
• can shop when shops are quiet
• can spend more time with children and grandchildren
• can do voluntary work

Income

This change in lifestyle could mean a substantial decrease in income, leading to a lower standard of living.

People in this situation may economize or try to make things easier by:
- buying cheaper cuts of meat
- buying saving stamps to help with budgeting
- becoming more conscious of the cost of fuel
- spending less money on clothes
- being more careful when shopping.

On the other hand, the elderly have many entitlements:
- free prescriptions
- free chiropody
- cheaper travel on public transport
- cold weather payments
- concessionary rates for theatre, leisure activities, hairdressers and many other services.

Food

Elderly people tend to be less active and have to budget on a smaller income. They may live alone or have some form of **disability**, resulting in a lack of interest in food or ability to prepare meals.

People in this age-group need to pay special attention to their food requirements otherwise their health may suffer. They need:
- foods which are low in fat, salt and energy ..... to lessen the risk of coronary heart disease, obesity, strokes and related disorders
- foods which are rich in vitamins and minerals ..... to promote strong bones, prevent osteomalacia, osteoporosis and anaemia, and infections
- limited carbohydrate but lots of fibre ..... as they are inactive, but need fibre to help them to have healthy bowel movements.

Nutritional needs

NUTRIENTS	FUNCTIONS
High fibre	to prevent constipation, diverticulitis
Vitamin B	to help make red blood cells and release energy
Vitamin C	to heal wounds, stop infection, and promote healthy gums and skin
Vitamin D	to help the body absorb calcium
Iron	to prevent anaemia
Protein	for cell replacement
Calcium	for teeth and bones

The elderly also need to take some exercise to keep their muscles active and their circulatory system in good working order.

Housing needs

As people get older they experience many physical changes. Their skin, hair, eyesight, hearing and senses may deteriorate or become less acute. Some develop teeth and gum disease, chest problems, digestive problems and less efficient kidneys. Other illnesses such as osteoporosis, arthritis and reduced mobility may occur.

Provision for these changing needs may require alterations in the home.

Stairlift

Hand rail and seat in shower

Many elderly people are unable to live alone, through illness, disability or lack of mobility. They may have to be cared for by their family or in the community.

Sheltered housing
- a warden on call for emergencies
- own flat/living unit
- a degree of independence.

Nursing homes
- 24-hour nursing care
- own room
- full care with meals.

Geriatric wards in hospital
- especially for bedridden people or people in need of medical care.

Residential care
- 24-hour care
- for mobile people who need to be cared for (should people require special medical care, they would be transferred to a hospital geriatric ward).

Support services
- person remains at home and is attended by support services (local authorities), home help, meals on wheels, day centres, mobile libraries, etc.
- carers.

Caring for an elderly family member

Families are encouraged to care for their elderly relatives in their own home. Such a responsibility can be rewarding but can also lead to stress and conflict. Relationships can become strained and difficult.

AN ELDERLY FAMILY MEMBER IN THE HOME

Negative aspects
- may be difficult and demanding
- may interfere
- may restrict family routines and activities
- may be critical of family behaviour
- may be forgetful
- may be a danger
- may give unwanted advice

Positive aspects
- may pass on skills and knowledge
- may babysit and help with children
- may act as mother/father substitute
- could spend time with adolescents
- could add to income
- could pass on family traditions
- could spoil the children
- could help with homework

KEY WORDS
disability
mobility
retirement

SUMMARY

● Elderly retired people have more free time to pursue interests and activities.
● Many retired people find it difficult to adjust to their new lifestyle.
● There are many facilities available to meet the needs of the elderly.
● Retirement may mean a lower standard of living.
● A nutritious diet is essential at this stage of the life cycle.
● Housing requirements change.
● The family may be responsible for the care of an elderly relative.

· ·

QUESTIONS

1 Suggest six suitable pastimes in which an elderly person could become involved.

2 In what ways might an elderly person adapt to a lower income?

3 List six essential nutrients in the diet of an elderly person, giving reasons why they are important.

4 Your grandmother is coming to live with you. She is confined to a wheelchair. What adjustments would have to be made to:
   a your home
   b your lifestyle?

Stress and conflict within the family

Stress

Anxiety is a normal, healthy emotion which everyone experiences. Feeling anxious keeps you on your toes, sharpens your senses and produces adrenaline, which improves your performance. **Stress** occurs when people become over-anxious and cannot cope with everyday pressures.

FACTORS WHICH CONTRIBUTE TO INCREASED STRESS LEVELS

- being tired
- being tense
- being run-down

SOME SITUATIONS WHICH CAN CAUSE STRESS

- examinations
- unemployment
- poverty
- divorce
- illness
- career choice
- abortion
- learning to drive
- debt
- moving house
- separation
- death
- conflict
- bullying
- miscarriage
- drugs
- alcohol
- redundancy
- starting school
- peer pressure
- pregnancy
- bringing up children

Effects of stress

anxiety attacks · low self-esteem · aggression · difficulty sleeping · short-temper · ulcers · headaches · disrupted eating patterns · over-indulgence in food, alcohol, cigarettes · illness · moodiness · suicide · mental breakdown · depression · strained relationships · apathy

Conflict

Everyone experiences some kind of **conflict**. These may be mild disagreements or differences of opinions within the family, in the workplace, with those in authority and sometimes with friends.

Some conflicts can be easily managed. Others are more serious and can cause the complete breakdown of a relationship.

FACTORS WHICH AFFECT CONFLICT SITUATIONS
• nature of the disagreement • age of the people involved • personalities involved • lack of emotional control • inability to communicate • instability → personal   → relationships

SOME SITUATIONS WHICH CAN CAUSE CONFLICT	
• religious differences	• marital problems
• ethnic differences	• drugs
• lack of organization	• alcohol
• sibling rivalry	• money management
• adolescent behaviour	• poor home management
• generation gap	

Effects of conflict

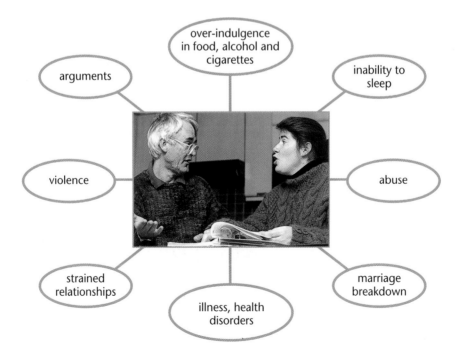

arguments

over-indulgence in food, alcohol and cigarettes

inability to sleep

violence

abuse

strained relationships

illness, health disorders

marriage breakdown

Management of stress and conflict

PREVENTING STRESS
- get organized
- delegate responsibilities
- think ahead
- talk to someone
- pace yourself
- get plenty of rest
- eat properly
- take up a leisure
  pursuit/hobby

PREVENTING CONFLICT
- diffuse the situation before it starts
- think before you speak
- listen
- try to see other person's point of view
- make allowances
- talk/communicate
- practise self-control
- avoid confrontation
- avoid heated arguments

DEALING WITH STRESS
- learn to relax
- talk to someone
- seek help
- think positive
- take control
- be assertive
- get organized
- prioritize

DEALING WITH CONFLICT
- negotiate
- calm down
- keep an open mind
- keep open a line of
  communication
- try to reach a compromise
- ask for advice
- seek professional help
  self-control

KEY WORDS
communication
compromise
conflict
management
negotiation
prevention
stress

SUMMARY

- Anxiety is a normal, healthy emotion.
- Stress occurs when a person cannot cope.
- Stress is brought about by many factors.
- Stress can cause ill-health.
- Everyone is likely to experience some kind of conflict.
- Conflict may occur at any stage of the life cycle.
- A number of strategies can be used to prevent and manage stress and conflict.

QUESTIONS

1 List ten factors which can cause stress.

2 Jane's parents refuse to let her go to the disco. She feels frustrated, angry and really uptight. What is the best way for Jane to deal with this situation?

3 Identify and explain the stress factors that a full-time working mother with three young children may experience.

4 Refer to Question 3. Outline strategies the mother could adopt to make her life easier.

SECTION 2
Diet and health

CHAPTER 12

Dietary guidelines and eating patterns

Current dietary recommendations

Nutrition is the process of feeding our bodies. No single food contains all the nutrients. We need to eat a wide variety of foods, if we are to remain healthy. In the western world there is a huge range of foods available, which should make it easy to follow a healthy eating pattern. However, many people in the west make poor food choices, resulting in various nutritional disorders. In response to this, the British government has taken steps to improve the health of the nation. It set up the Committee on Medical Aspects of Food Policy (**COMA**), which published a national food guide called *The Balance of Good Health*. This publication aims to help people to understand and enjoy healthy eating.

The Balance of Good Health suggests eight guidelines for a healthy diet. If you follow these guidelines as far as you can, you will feel well, look good and enjoy life:

- enjoy your food
- eat a variety of different foods
- eat the right amount to be a healthy weight
- eat plenty of foods rich in starch and fibre
- don't eat too much fat
- don't eat sugary foods too often
- look after the vitamins in your food
- if you drink alcohol, keep within sensible limits.

It suggests you use the five-portioned plate shown in the picture to help choose the food you eat.

The Balance of Good Health

Fruit and vegetables
Choose a wide variety

Bread, other cereals and potatoes
Eat all types and choose high fibre kinds whenever you can

Meat, fish and alternatives
Choose lower fat alternatives whenever you can

Fatty and sugary foods
Try not to eat these too often, and when you do, have small amounts

Milk and dairy foods
Choose lower fat alternatives whenever you can

Why do people choose as they do

People may have some knowledge of foods that are good for them, but they do not always make healthy choices. There are many different reasons why people choose particular foods. Personal food choices and food habits are called **eating patterns**. These patterns can be adopted from childhood and are often influenced by parental attitudes. Habits may change as people get older and as more and different influences take effect.

Lifestyle

Daily routine and **lifestyle** will affect the time of the day at which meals are eaten, where they are eaten, and how much time is taken to eat them.

- work (e.g. shift working, part-time jobs)
- health (e.g. diabetics must eat at regular intervals)
- age (e.g. adolescents tend to be in a rush, often eating a lot of fast foods)

IMPLICATIONS

People are tempted by snacking, ready-made meals, fast foods, convenience foods, irregular eating, foods high in fat and sugar, and low in fibre.

Media

Food manufacturers use different **media** to influence and persuade people to try new and different products.

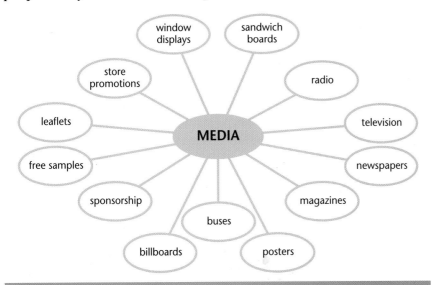

IMPLICATIONS

People are tempted to try new foods. They become interested, want the foods and convince themselves that they would be a worthwhile purchase.

Foreign influences

People's eating habits have changed over the years from traditional foods to include food from around the world.

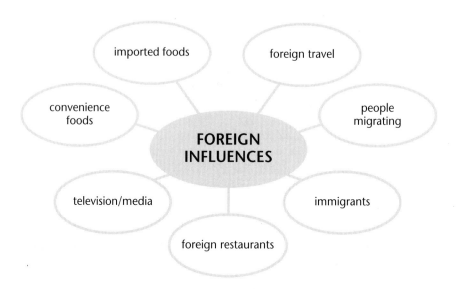

IMPLICATIONS

People now eat a more varied diet and are more inclined to be adventurous, trying new and foreign foods.

Religion

Religious beliefs influence many people in their eating habits. Some religions have quite strict food laws.

Religious festivals (e.g. Christmas, Easter, Shrove Tuesday, Ramadan) are usually associated with particular foods.

- Jews (do not eat pork as the pig is considered unclean)
- Muslims (do not eat pork)
- Hindus (do not eat meat from a cow as the cow is sacred)
- Mormons (do not drink tea or coffee)

IMPLICATIONS

Certain groups of people will not eat or drink certain foods. They may cook their food according to strict laws.

Fashion trends

There are certain trends or **fashions** associated with the choice of food. Some diets are short-lived 'fads', others may be followed for health reasons. Some young people can be very health conscious, because of body image and emphasis on leisure.

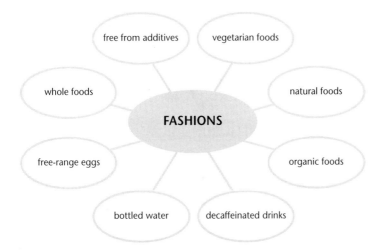

free from additives

vegetarian foods

whole foods

natural foods

FASHIONS

free-range eggs

organic foods

bottled water

decaffeinated drinks

IMPLICATIONS

People may choose not to eat certain foods, opting for 'healthier' alternatives.

Cultural/traditional influences

Culture is defined by the customs and habits of a particular country. Food is part of a country's culture, determined by **tradition**, lifestyle, climate, wealth, etc. Some foods are associated with particular festivals (very often religious).

Food
- Ireland (Irish stew, soda bread, potato bread)
- Italy (spaghetti bolognese, lasagne)
- China (sweet and sour, chow mein)
- France (croissants, baguettes, brie)
- India (curry, naan, chapatis)
- USA (hamburgers, waffles, coke)

Festivals
- Christmas (turkey, mince pies)
- Shrove Tuesday (pancakes)
- Hallowe'en (toffee apples, pumpkin pie)
- Easter (Simnel cake, hot cross buns, roast pork)

IMPLICATIONS

Ways of eating are passed from generation to generation and from family to family.

KEY WORDS

COMA
culture
eating patterns
fashion
lifestyle
media
religious beliefs
tradition

SUMMARY

- COMA has issued eight guidelines for a healthy diet.
- Eating patterns are influenced by lifestyle, the media, other countries, religion, fashion and culture.

. . . .

QUESTIONS

1 State the eight guidelines for healthy eating.
2 Outline the factors which influence people's eating patterns.
3 Evaluate the diet of this adolescent in the light of current guidelines.

JENNY, AGED 16	
Breakfast:	cup of coffee with milk and sugar
Lunch:	white bread sandwiches with tuna or salad or egg filling, cola drink
Evening meal:	burger or pizza or stir fry or tinned spaghetti, with chips, cola drink
Snacks:	biscuits, crisps, sometimes an apple

Nutrients

Nutrients are chemical substances contained in food. Foods have to be digested (broken down) so that the nutrients can be absorbed into the body.

There are five groups of nutrients:

- **protein**
- **fats**
- **carbohydrates**
- **vitamins**
- **minerals.**

Non-starch polysaccharride (NSP) and **water** are not nutrients.

Water must be taken daily to replace that which is used and lost through daily living.

NSP, found in carbohydrate foods, is not digested, but passes through the body taking waste and unwanted substances with it in the faeces.

Protein

Found in	ANIMAL	VEGETABLE
	meat	peas
	fish	beans
	eggs	lentils
	milk	nuts
	cheese	cereals

Function   To build and repair skin, hair, nails, bones, muscles and many other body tissues. Also used for energy if there is not enough carbohydrate available.

Deficiency   Kwashiorkor

Child suffering from kwashiorkor syndrome in refugee camp, Somalia

Fats

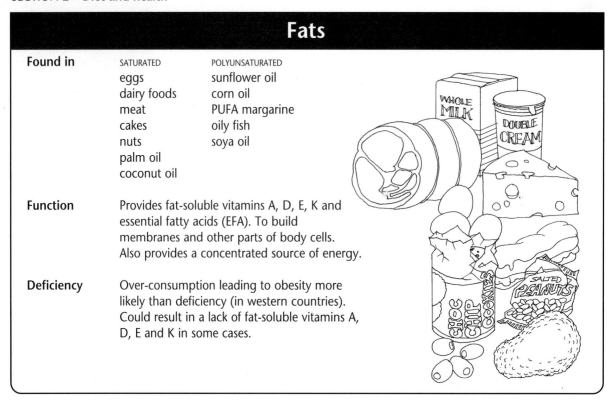

Found in	SATURATED	POLYUNSATURATED
	eggs	sunflower oil
	dairy foods	corn oil
	meat	PUFA margarine
	cakes	oily fish
	nuts	soya oil
	palm oil	
	coconut oil	

Function — Provides fat-soluble vitamins A, D, E, K and essential fatty acids (EFA). To build membranes and other parts of body cells. Also provides a concentrated source of energy.

Deficiency — Over-consumption leading to obesity more likely than deficiency (in western countries). Could result in a lack of fat-soluble vitamins A, D, E and K in some cases.

Carbohydrates

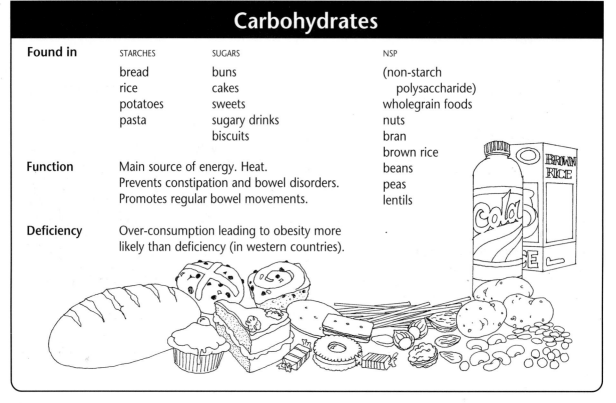

Found in	STARCHES	SUGARS	NSP
	bread	buns	(non-starch polysaccharide)
	rice	cakes	wholegrain foods
	potatoes	sweets	nuts
	pasta	sugary drinks	bran
		biscuits	brown rice
			beans
			peas
			lentils

Function — Main source of energy. Heat. Prevents constipation and bowel disorders. Promotes regular bowel movements.

Deficiency — Over-consumption leading to obesity more likely than deficiency (in western countries).

Vitamins

Vitamin A (retinol)

Found in

milk
butter
cheese
eggs
liver
fatty fish
fish oils
margarine
red and yellow fruit
carrots
green vegetables

Function

Helps the eyes to see in dim light.
Helps linings in the body to stay moist.

Deficiency

Can cause night blindness.

Vitamin C (ascorbic acid)

Found in

citrus fruits
green vegetables
new potatoes
berries

Function

Makes connective tissue to hold the cells together
Helps body absorb iron.
Helps resist infection.

Deficiency

Cuts take time to heal.
Skin becomes spotty.
Serious deficiency causes scurvy.

Vitamin D (cholecalciferol)

Found in

oily fish
fish liver oils
eggs
margarine
liver
milk
butter

Function

Helps to make strong bones and teeth.
Helps broken bones heal and aids the absorption of calcium.

Deficiency

Causes soft bones in children.
Slows growth.
Serious deficiency causes rickets.

Vitamin E (tocopherol)

Found in

wholegrain cereals
corn oil
soya oil
margarine
liver

Function

May help fertility.

Deficiency

Unknown at this time.

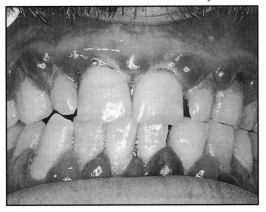

Mouth of person suffering from scurvy

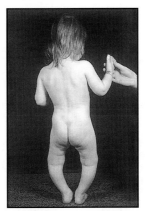

Child suffering from rickets

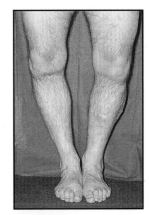

Bowed legs of a middle-aged man suffering from rickets

Vitamins

Vitamin B₁ (thiamin)

Found in

white flour
wholegrain cereals
meat
eggs
breakfast cereals

Function

Helps carbohydrate to make energy.
Helps the nervous system.
Helps growth.

Deficiency

Causes tiredness and depression.
Serious deficiency causes beri beri.

Vitamin B₂ (riboflavin)

Found in

offal
wholegrain cereals
fish
meat
eggs
pulses
cheese

Function

Helps make energy from fat and proteins.

Deficiency

Slows growth.
Causes skin, eye and mouth infections.

Vitamin B₃ (niacin)

Found in

wholegrain cereals
meat
offal
pulses
peanuts
white flour

Function

Helps make energy.
Helps growth.
Helps make healthy skin.

Deficiency

Serious deficiency causes pellagra.

Vitamin B₁₂ (cobalamin)

Found in

foods of animal origin
liver
fish
meat
cheese
milk
eggs
fortified breakfast cereals
May be deficient in a strict vegetarian or vegan diet.

Function

Helps prevent certain forms of anaemia.
Helps cells to divide.
Protects the nervous system.

Deficiency

Pernicious anaemia and neurological problems.

Folate (folic acid) (vitamin B group)

Found in

dark green vegetables   pulses
wholegrain cereals   offal

Function

Helps make red blood cells.

Deficiency

Causes tiredness or anaemia.

Vitamin B₆ (pyridoxine)

Found in

yeast   poultry
wholegrain cereals   meat
most vegetables   fish

Function

Needed for healthy teeth and gums, the nervous system and red blood cells.

Deficiency

May cause skin damage or damage to the nervous system

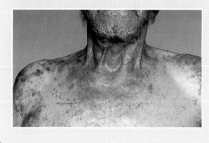

Man suffering from Pellagra

Minerals

Iron

Found in

offal
eggs
red meat
dried fruit
white bread
chocolate

Function

Needed to make
red blood cells.

Deficiency

Tiredness.
Can cause
anaemia.

Calcium

Found in

milk
cheese
fish
white flour

Function

Needed for bones
and teeth, and for
clotting blood.

Deficiency

Poor bones and
teeth.
Can cause rickets.
Poor muscle and
nerve function.

Fluoride

Found in

fluoride toothpaste
drinking water
seafood

Function

Involved in the
formation of bones
and teeth. Helps
them resist decay.

Deficiency

A deficiency is rare.
Excessive amounts
can cause mottling
of teeth.

Water

Found in

all foods in variable
amounts but
especially in fruit and
vegetables

Function

Major part of all
body fluids.
Helps digestion and
absorption of
nutrients.
Assists removal of
waste.
Helps control body
temperature.
Lubricates joints and
membranes.

Deficiency

Dehydration.

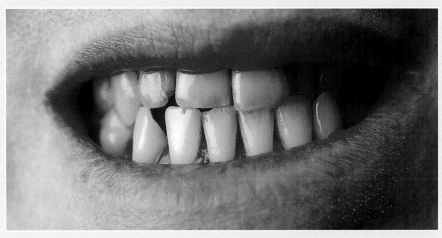

One of the effects of calcium deficiency is poor bones and teeth

SUMMARY

- There are five main nutrients present in food.
- The body also requires water and NSP.
- The nutrients are used to build, protect and insulate the body.

QUESTIONS

1 List the five main nutrients and give one good source of each.

2 What are the other two substances needed by the body. Explain why these are important in the diet. Give examples of sources of each.

3 Kwashiorkor, scurvy, rickets, beri beri, pellagra, anaemia, osteoporosis and night blindness are diseases caused by a nutrient deficiency. Fill in the table below, identifying the deficient nutrient in each case.

DEFICIENCY DISEASE	DEFICIENT NUTRIENT(S)
kwashiorkor	
scurvy	
rickets	
beri beri	
pellagra	
anaemia	
osteoporosis	
night blindness	

4 Make a list of the foods you ate yesterday. Draw up a chart with the headings: PROTEIN, FAT, CARBOHYDRATE, MINERALS, VITAMINS. Sort your list of foods under the headings.

Evaluate your nutrient intake for the day using the information in this chapter and your own knowledge.

Nutritional needs at key stages in the life cycle

The foods a person eats influences his/her health, so it is important to eat wisely. The body can be prone to faults and weaknesses if it is poorly maintained. A person's **nutritional needs** vary at each **key stage** of his/her life.

The Department of Health has compiled charts indicating an individual's requirements for energy and nutrients. The figures are given as:

Dietary Reference Values (DRVs)
These are given for particular groups of people. They are not meant to be specific targets for individuals.

Reference Nutrient Intake (RNI)
This is the maximum amount of a nutrient recommended per person.

Estimated Average Requirement (EAR)
This is an estimated *average* amount of a nutrient recommended per person.

Babies/toddlers (0–3 years)

Babies and toddlers should be encouraged to eat a wide range of foods of different textures and discouraged from developing poor eating habits.

Protein	**for growth**
Calcium	**for bones and teeth**
Vitamins A and D	**for teeth and bones**
Iron	**to prevent anaemia**

- before the age of six months babies should be given gluten-free foods
- babies under the age of six months should not be given cow's milk
- do not give snacks, especially sweets and crisps which are of low nutritional value
- encourage good eating habits
- do not give too many NSP foods as these are too filling. The child will be unable to eat sufficient food to sustain them
- give full fat milk and other dairy products until the age of five
- limit the amount of sugary and fatty foods eaten
- give foods low in salt and sugar
- ensure they have plenty of raw fruit and vegetables to promote strong teeth and gums

Primary school child (4–11 years)

The primary school child can be easily influenced by advertising, peer pressure and family diet. They should be encouraged to maintain a good, well balanced diet and regular meal times.

Protein	for rapid growth
Calcium	for rapid growth
Iron	for blood
Vitamins A and D	for teeth and bones
Energy foods	for energy

- give full fat milk until the age of five
- use whole foods, raw fruit and vegetables for NSP
- provide energy foods according to energy needs and appetite
- encourage healthy and regular meals
- avoid and discourage snacks and 'junk' foods

Adolescent (12–17 years)

From the age of 12 adolescents grow rapidly. Their energy needs are high.

Protein	for growth spurt
Calcium	teeth and bones
Iron	especially for girls due to menstrual loss
Vitamins	absorption of minerals
Energy foods	increased energy requirements

- provides energy foods according to activity (balance input with output)
- fruit and vegetables provide NSP and promote healthy skin
- fats should be restricted, may cause acne or weight problems
- drinks, especially water, will help keep skin clear

Young adult/adult (18–64 years)

The young adult diet should reflect the lifestyle and energy output, observing dietary guidelines to maintain a good standard of health.

Protein	repair and replace cells
Energy foods	requirements vary depending on activity
Iron	important for women
Calcium	for replacement
NSP	for regular bowel movements and prevention of bowel disorders

- fat intake should be restricted, especially saturated fat (animal), to avoid coronary heart disease and/or obesity
- high fibre diet recommended to avoid constipation, etc.
- low salt diet to avert high blood pressure problems
- women should eat foods rich in calcium to reduce the chance of osteoporosis
- women should take iron-rich foods to prevent anaemia

Elderly (65+ years)

Elderly people require fewer energy-dense foods as they are likely to be less active in their advancing years. They need a well-balanced diet rich in protective nutrients.

Protein	for repair and replacement of cells
NSP	to prevent constipation
Calcium	to strengthen teeth and bones (ageing bones can be very brittle)
Iron	to prevent anaemia
Vitamin B	to release energy and for healthy nerves
Vitamin C	to prevent infection and for healthy skin and gums
Vitamin D	to assist the absorption of calcium

- foods need to be easy to digest, e.g. fish
- avoid animal fats to prevent weight gain
- nutrients provided should be in a concentrated form (low in fat but rich in other nutrients)
- vitamins are important as they prevent scurvy and may protect against colds, flu and infections

Pregnant women

Whilst it is not necessary to 'eat for two', food eaten should be concentrated sources of nutrients.

Protein	for the developing foetus, milk production and to maintain the mother's body
Iron	to prevent anaemia and to produce red blood cells for the foetus
Calcium, Vitamins A and D	for healthy bones and teeth in mother and good bone formation in baby
NSP	to avoid constipation
Folate (folic acid)	reduces the risk of birth defects, e.g. spina bifida

- eat a good variety of protein-rich foods
- dark green vegetables and red meat, along with food rich in Vitamin C, to help absorption of iron
- avoid saturated fats (animal)
- eat plenty of dairy produce and fish
- avoid soft cheeses as these may cause listeria which can result in miscarriage and still-birth
- eat plenty of wholemeal foods, fruit, vegetables and water for vitamins B and C } promotes regular bowel movement
- broccoli, breakfast cereals, bread and nuts for iron and folic acid }
- low salt diet to avert high blood pressure

Vegetarians

There are two types of vegetarian.

Lacto vegetarian
Lacto vegetarians do not eat animal flesh but will eat animal products such as milk, cheese, yoghurt, butter and cream.

Vegan
Vegans do not eat any foods from animal sources. Their diet consists of fruit, vegetables, nuts and cereals.

Protein	for growth and repair
Fats	for energy and essential fatty acids
Minerals	for bones, teeth and blood
Iron, calcium,	prevention of anaemia
vitamins B_{12}	and to produce red blood cells

- food sources must be from vegetables, soya, textured vegetable protein, nuts, seeds and pulses. Lacto vegetarians can get protein from milk and cheese, etc.
- fats must come from vegetable oils, nuts, seeds, olives and dairy produce
- minerals can come from eggs, cereals, green vegetables, nuts and pulses. Lots of vitamin C is required to assist absorption of iron
- bread, leafy green vegetables, dried fruit, tofu, nuts and seeds will provide some minerals
- B_{12} will be provided by yeast extract, breakfast cereals and soya milk

SUMMARY

● Nutritional needs vary at each key stage of the life cycle.
● The Department of Health has compiled charts to help people work out their nutritional requirements.

QUESTIONS

1 Explain the difference between the diet of a lacto vegetarian and that of a vegan.

2 Why should elderly people choose foods:
   a which are low in energy
   b which are low in fat
   c which are rich in vitamins?

3 Mary is pregnant. She is pale and tired and lacks energy. Give two reasons why Mary may be feeling like this.
   Suggest three evening meals that will ensure her dietary needs are met, indicating the nutrients present.

4 a Why is it important for the following groups of people to have an adequate intake of calcium and vitamin D:
   i   a pregnant woman
   ii babies and primary school children
   iii the elderly?
   b Use the food tables in Chapters 13 and 14 to find out the daily nutritional requirements of the above groups of people.

Diet-related disorders

Although most people in the west have plenty to eat, some suffer from health disorders which are the result of unwise food choices. Some of the disorders are caused by the excess of a nutrient and others by lack of a nutrient.

Coronary heart disease
Causes of coronary heart disease

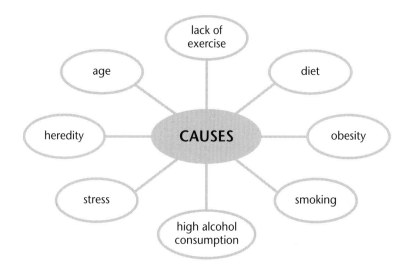

A healthy heart is one that functions efficiently, where the arteries are clear and through which the blood flows easily.

Diets which contain large amounts of saturated fats increase the level of cholesterol in the blood. This excess cholesterol deposits itself along the walls of the arteries, causing them to reduce in size.

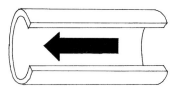

NORMAL ARTERY
blood can flow through normally

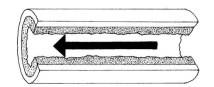

PARTLY BLOCKED ARTERY
blood flow is restricted

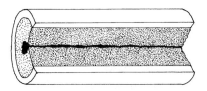

BADLY BLOCKED ARTERY
blood cannot flow through

This is called **atherosclerosis** of the arteries (sometimes referred to as the hardening of the arteries) and is especially dangerous in the coronary arteries as these two arteries supply the heart muscle. As the opening in the arteries becomes smaller, circulation slows down and blood pressure increases. The heart has to work harder to pump the blood around the body resulting in:

- shortness of breath
- palpitations
- chest pains.

CHOLESTEROL

Cholesterol is a type of fat which occurs naturally in the body. It is also present in foods that contain saturated fats, e.g. butter, meat, cream, cheese, etc.

Sources of cholesterol	Sources of saturated fat	Sources of polyunsaturated fat
egg yolk	suet, lard, dripping	sunflower seed oil, corn oil,
offal	butter, cream	peanut oil and soybean oil
shellfish	hard cheese	soft margarines
dairy products	hard margarine	most nuts
		oily fish

Dietary implications

- cut down on saturated (animal) fats, use polyunsaturated (vegetable) fats instead
- eat plenty of fruit and vegetables
- eat plenty of high fibre (NSP) foods. Fibre should help in the breakdown of cholesterol
- replace red meat with fish and poultry
- cut down on hidden fats in biscuits, cakes and most snack foods
- reduce salt to avoid high blood pressure
- grill, poach, microwave or bake food instead of frying.

Other ways to prevent coronary heart disease

- take plenty of exercise
- do not smoke
- reduce alcohol intake
- avoid worry or stress
- reduce weight (if necessary).

Obesity

When a person is 20 percent over the recommended weight for their height and build, they are said to be obese.

Obesity is a serious health hazard. It is generally accepted that people gain weight as they get older and most obese people are adult, but obesity can affect babies, children and young adults.

Causes of obesity

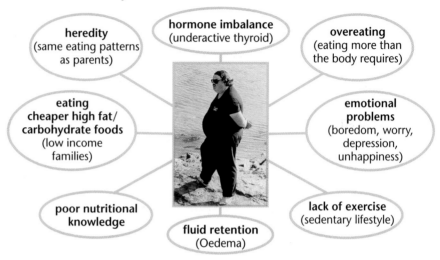

heredity
(same eating patterns
as parents)

hormone imbalance
(underactive thyroid)

overeating
(eating more than
the body requires)

eating
cheaper high fat/
carbohydrate foods
(low income
families)

emotional
problems
(boredom, worry,
depression,
unhappiness)

poor nutritional
knowledge

lack of exercise
(sedentary lifestyle)

fluid retention
(Oedema)

Dietary implications

- reduce kilojoule intake
- have three meals a day and avoid snacks inbetween
- replace saturated fats (use skimmed milk, lean meat, white fish and chicken)
- grill, poach, bake or microwave food instead of frying
- reduce carbohydrate intake (i.e. sugar, white bread, biscuits) and replace it with high fibre (NSP) foods instead (i.e. wholemeal bread, cereals and brown rice)
- cut down on sugary drinks and alcohol and drink plenty of water instead
- eat plenty of fresh fruit and vegetables.

Other ways to prevent obesity

- take regular exercise
- consult doctor for advice
- avoid crash diets
- join a slimming club to provide support and motivation.

PROBLEMS ASSOCIATED WITH OBESITY

- low self-esteem
- accidents are more common
- diabetes
- gall bladder problems
- respiratory problems
- heart disease
- infertility in women
- osteoarthritis
- toxaemia and difficulty in childbirth
- varicose veins
- shorter life expectancy

Anorexia nervosa

Anorexia nervosa is an eating disorder characterized by self-inflicted starvation which results in extreme weight loss. It is not clear why a person develops anorexia. Some reasons might be:

- family conflict
- fear of growing up and anxiety about his/her own sexuality
- sexual abuse
- emotional stress.

Anorexia nervosa is very common in adolescent girls aged between 12 and 18, but it can be seen in older people and, more recently, in young boys. It occurs primarily in western society, especially among the middle and upper social classes.

People with anorexia nervosa have a real terror about putting on weight. They tend to see themselves as fat and getting fatter. They will think about food nearly all the time and usually enjoy cooking and seeing other people eat. Sometimes it can be hard to recognize that someone is suffering from anorexia nervosa. When they get help it is usually psychological and psychiatric.

Possible effects of anorexia nervosa

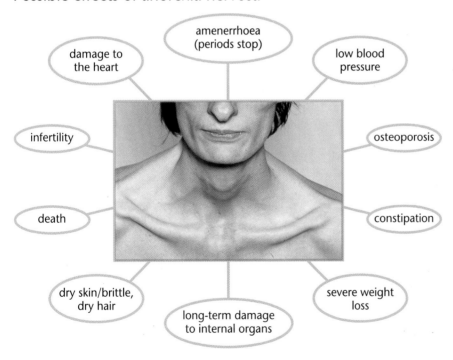

amenerrhoea (periods stop)

damage to the heart

low blood pressure

infertility

osteoporosis

death

constipation

dry skin/brittle, dry hair

long-term damage to internal organs

severe weight loss

Dietary implications

- develop a controlled, healthy, eating pattern
- eat small, regular, high-energy meals and build up quantity slowly
- weight gain is vital.

Other ways to manage the disorder

- psychiatric help
- emotional support
- counselling
- treatment centres
- on-going monitoring.

Bulimia nervosa

Bulimia nervosa is an eating disorder characterized by the consumption of large amounts of high calorie foods (binge eating) followed by self-induced vomiting. Bulimics are often slightly overweight but their weight fluctuates continuously. Bulimics are often afraid of becoming fat and have a distorted image of what shape and size they are. They may use slimming tablets and laxatives to control their weight. They often eat in private thus hiding their problem.

Bulimia is common in young adult women between the ages of 18 and 25.

There is no single cause of this eating disorder. Possible reasons include:

- emotional shock or grief
- stress over a period of time
- fear of growing up
- an unhappy childhood
- unhappiness about body shape or size
- unhappy relationships within the family
- a need to have control over one's life.

Possible effects of bulimia nervosa

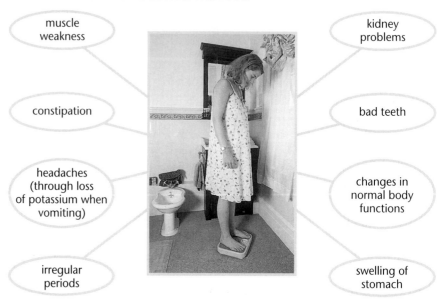

muscle weakness

kidney problems

constipation

bad teeth

headaches (through loss of potassium when vomiting)

changes in normal body functions

irregular periods

swelling of stomach

Ways to manage the disorder
- visit the doctor or dietician regularly
- counselling and therapy
- dental care
- restore a normal eating pattern
- hospitalization.

Osteoporosis

Osteoporosis is a natural part of ageing. As people get older their bone density decreases and bones become more brittle and fracture easily. A calcium deficiency makes the condition worse. Women are more at risk than men as childbirth and menstruation uses up available calcium. At the age of 30 and older, calcium lost from bones cannot be replaced. It is important to eat a diet high in calcium during childhood and adolescence.

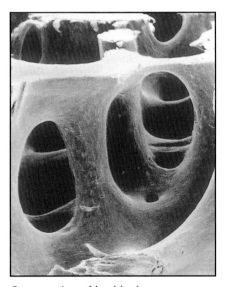

Cross-section of healthy bone.

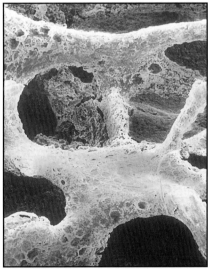

Cross-section of bone suffering from osteoporosis.

Causes of osteoporosis
- calcium deficiency in the diet
- vitamin D deficiency preventing absorption of calcium
- phytic acid present in cereal husks makes calcium unavailable to the body
- oxalic acid in rhubarb and strawberries inhibits calcium absorption
- fatty acids present during digestion may inhibit calcium absorption
- large amounts of protein may cause calcium excretion in the urine
- smoking inhibits calcium absorption.

Dietary implications

- eat white bread and cereals which have been fortified with calcium
- eat a variety of dairy produce
- ensure a good supply of vitamin D (sunlight, margarine and oily fish)
- eat plenty of fruit and vegetables, especially dark green vegetables
- eat a good supply of phosphorous which can assist calcium in the strengthening of teeth and bones (meat, fish, eggs and dairy produce, cereals and green vegetables).

Other ways to prevent osteoporosis

- take regular exercise to strengthen bones and increase their mineral content
- avoid smoking and drinking large amounts of alcohol
- consult doctor for medical advice.

Anaemia

Anaemia is caused by iron deficiency. Iron is essential. It makes haemoglobin, which gives red blood cells their colour. Haemoglobin carries oxygen to every cell of the body. Without oxygen, cells work inefficiently. People who suffer from anaemia may feel tired and lacking in energy.

Possible symptoms

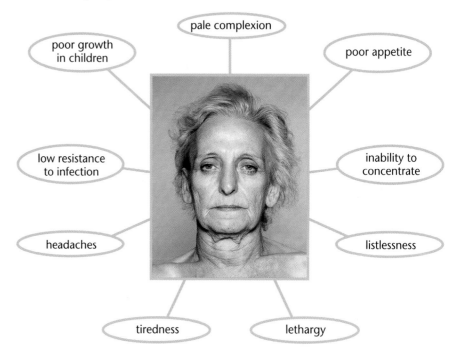

Causes

- limited intake of iron-rich foods
- inadequate absorption of iron
- heavy menstruation
- lack of iron replacement after surgery and childbirth
- insufficient iron during growth spurt
- insufficient iron during pregnancy
- vegetarian diets which lack easily absorbed iron (from animal sources)
- babies not given sufficient variety of foods to provide iron during weaning.

SOURCES OF IRON

Foods rich in iron need to be taken regularly. Iron comes in two forms: haem iron and non-haem iron:
- haem iron resembles human blood and is available from animal sources. It is easily absorbed
- non-haem iron is available from vegetable sources and is not so easily absorbed. Non-haem iron must be converted from a ferric state (non-haem) to a more absorbable, ferrous state.

Vitamin C (ascorbic acid) increases the body's ability to absorb iron, especially that from plant foods.

Sources of haem iron (easily absorbed)
- lean red meat
- liver
- kidneys
- black pudding
- poultry
- game
- corned beef

Vitamin C-rich foods
- citrus fruits
- blackcurrants
- green vegetables

Sources of non-haem iron (difficult to absorb)
- watercress
- green leafy vegetables
- dried fruit
- wholegrain cereals
- bread
- pulses
- curry powder
- chocolate
- eggs

Some foods reduce the body's ability to absorb iron, e.g. tannin (in tea), oxalates and phytic acid (from bran foods):
- reduce tea intake
- eat *white* bread which has been fortified with iron.

Dental caries

Foods containing sugar are the main causes of tooth decay. When people eat or drink, plaque (a mixture of saliva, food and bacteria) forms on their teeth. The plaque, when exposed to sugar, produces acid. Acid attacks the enamel of teeth resulting in tooth decay. Each time sugary foods are eaten, acid levels remain high for at least 20 minutes. Children should be encouraged to eat sugary foods *less* often to minimize the occurrence of dental caries.

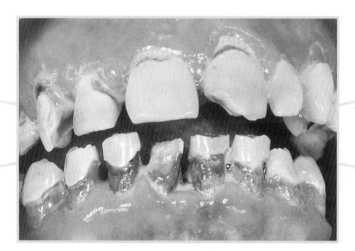

plaque build-up
+ sugar ⇒ acid

food lodges
and decays

enamel
erodes

gums become
inflamed

Dietary implications

- limit sugary food to mealtimes
- eat food rich in calcium and vitamin D, especially during childhood and adolescence
- eat raw, crisp fruit and vegetables
- choose sugar-free drinks
- avoid eating between meals.

Other ways to avoid tooth decay

- brush teeth at least twice a day
- use a fluoride toothpaste
- use a good quality toothbrush and replace regularly
- visit the dentist every six months
- do not abuse teeth, e.g. don't crack nuts
- dental floss teeth regularly.

SUMMARY

- Unwise food choice can result in health disorders.
- Coronary heart disease can be caused by many factors.
- Obesity is a serious health hazard.
- Bulimia and anorexia nervosa are physical and psychological eating disorders.
- Osteoporosis is a brittle bone disease often prevalent in old age.
- Excess sugar in the diet causes tooth decay.
- Anaemia is the result of a deficiency of iron.

KEY WORDS

anaemia
anorexia nervosa
atherosclerosis
bulimia nervosa
cholesterol
coronary heart disease
dental caries
obesity
osteoporosis

QUESTIONS

1 State five health disorders that may be related to poor diet.
2 List five possible causes of coronary heart disease, other than diet.
3 Why is obesity dangerous to health?
4 What is meant by the term:
  a anorexia nervosa
  b bulimia nervosa?
5 How could diet help to prevent osteoporosis?
6 Analyse the effect of a diet low in iron.
7 What advice would you give to a young child about the care of their teeth?

CHAPTER 16

Meal planning

When **planning meals** it is important to consider the following points:

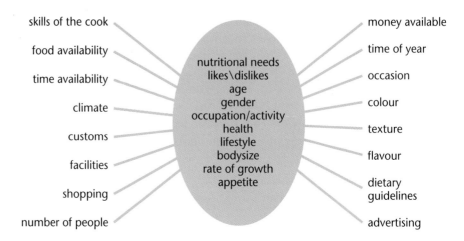

skills of the cook

food availability

time availability

climate

customs

facilities

shopping

number of people

nutritional needs
likes\dislikes
age
gender
occupation/activity
health
lifestyle
bodysize
rate of growth
appetite

money available

time of year

occasion

colour

texture

flavour

dietary
guidelines

advertising

Menu planning

A knowledge of **nutrition** is required to plan balanced and nutritious meals. A well-balanced diet contains all the nutrients the body requires in the correct proportions. A daily diet is usually made up of three meals:

● breakfast   ● lunch   ● dinner/tea

OR

● breakfast   ● dinner   ● tea.

Between them, these meals should supply an individual's daily nutritional needs. They should be made up of a mix of the five **food groups**.

When planning a menu, foods should be chosen following the **dietary guidelines** given in *The Balance of Good Health* (see Chapter 12). This will ensure a **balanced meal**.

Fatty and Sugary Foods

Butter, margarine, low fat spreads
Cooking oils, mayonaise and
salad dressings (oils)
Biscuits, cakes, puddings
Ice cream
Chocolate
Sweets
Crisps
Sugar
Sweetened drink

Use sparingly

Bread and Cereals

Bread, rolls, chapatis
Breakfast cereals, oats
Pasta, noodles
Rice
Potatoes, sweet potatoes
Dishes made from maize,
millet and cornmeal

Select 5 portions

Fruit and Vegetables

All fresh, frozen and canned
fruit and vegetables
Salad vegetables
Beans and lentils
Dried fruit and fruit juice

Select 5 portions

Milk and Dairy Produce

Milk
Cheese
Yoghurt
Fromage frais

Select 3 portions

Meat, Fish and Alternatives

Meat, beef, pork, bacon, lamb
Meat products, sausages,
beefburgers, meat pies
Poultry, chicken, turkey
Fish, fresh and frozen and canned
fish products, fish fingers, fish cakes
Offal, liver, kidney
Eggs
Beans and lentils, baked beans, chick peas
Nuts and nut products, peanut butter
TVP and other meat alternatives

Select 2 portions

Breakfast

This is the first meal of the day, and, having usually fasted for at least eight hours, it should not be missed out. Energy stores will be low and it is important to refuel the body for the day ahead. Having breakfast prevents hunger and tiredness during the morning, when one might be tempted to eat unhealthy snacks. Breakfast should be nutritious, quick and easy to prepare.

Breakfast 1

Fruit juice
Weetabix with semi-skimmed milk
Wholemeal toast
PUFA margarine
Poached egg
Tea (black no sugar)

Breakfast 2

Coco pops with whole milk

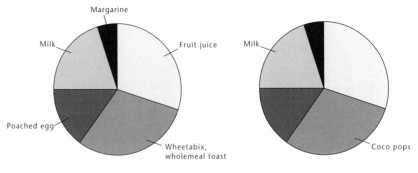

Advantages of breakfast 1

Food groups

fruit and vegetables (fruit juice) 🍎
bread and cereals (Weetabix, wholemeal toast) 🍞 🍞
milk and dairy produce (milk) 🐄
fatty and sugary foods (PUFA margarine)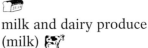
meat, fish and alternatives (egg) 🐟

Advantages of breakfast 2

Food groups

bread and cereals (cereal) 🍞

milk and dairy produce (milk) 🐄

Nutrition
protein (egg, milk)
carbohydrate (cereal, toast)
calcium (milk)
iron (Weetabix, egg, wholemeal bread)
vitamin A (egg, margarine, milk)
vitamin B (Weetabix, wholemeal bread)
vitamin C (fruit juice)
vitamin D (milk)

Nutrition
protein (cereal, milk)
carbohydrate (cereal)
calcium (milk)
iron (cereal)
vitamin A (cereal)
vitamin B (cereal)
vitamin D (milk)

Dietary guidelines
NSP in cereal and wholemeal toast
low fat (margarine, milk, poaching)
no added sugar
no added salt

Dietary guidelines
low fat (cereal)

Other advantages
- easy and quick to prepare
- would suit the whole family
- no waste
- colourful

Other advantages
- easy and quick to prepare
- cheap
- little washing up

Disadvantages of breakfast 1
- expensive
- requires a little preparation time
- a lot of washing up

Disadvantages of breakfast 2
- high in sugar
- high in salt
- only uses food from two food groups
- would only appeal to young children and teenagers
- low in vitamins
- additives present
- colourless

Lunch menu

Lunch 1
Egg and bacon quiche
Salad
Wheaten bread

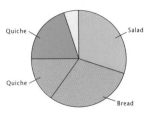

Lunch 2
Beans, sausage rolls and chips
Coke
Tomato sauce

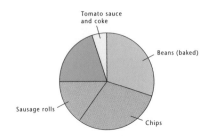

Advantages of lunch 1
Food groups
fruit and vegetables (lettuce, tomato, cucumber, onion, pepper)
meat, fish and alternatives (bacon)
milk and dairy produce (milk, cheese, eggs)
bread and cereals (wheaten bread, pastry)
fatty and sugary foods (bacon, pastry, salad dressing, low fat margarine)

Nutrition
protein (milk, eggs, bacon, cheese)
carbohydrate (pastry, wheaten bread)
calcium (milk, cheese, white flour [pastry], onion)
iron (eggs, milk, green vegetables, wheaten bread)
vitamin A (tomato, eggs, margarine, milk, cheese)
vitamin B (bacon, wheaten bread, pastry, eggs, onion)
vitamin C (lettuce, tomato, cucumber, peppers, onion)
vitamin D (milk, eggs, margarine, cheese)

Advantages of lunch 2
Food groups
fruit and vegetables (beans)
meat, fish and alternatives (sausages)
bread and cereals (chips, pastry)
fatty and sugary foods (pastry, chips, sausages, tomato sauce, coke)

Nutrition
protein (sausages, beans)
carbohydrate (potatoes)
calcium (flour, pork)
iron (beans, pork sausages)
vitamin B (beans, pastry, pork sausages)
vitamin D (margarine, pastry)

Dietary guidelines
low fat (PUFA margarine in pastry)
NSP (wheaten bread)
no added sugar
no added salt

Dietary guidelines
- high fat (sausage rolls, chips and method of cooking)
- NSP (in beans)
- sugar (high in coke and tomato sauce)
- salt (high in sausages and added salt)

Other advantages
- suitable for whole family, all age-groups
- can be bought ready-made
- can be served hot or cold
- uses food from all food groups
- colourful
- is different

Other advantages
- appeals mostly to children and teenagers
- can be bought and eaten immediately
- filling and satisfying/high satiety value
- familiar

Disadvantages of lunch 1
- expensive
- requires a lot of preparation
- may be waste

Disadvantages of lunch 2
- high in fat
- does not contain sufficient vitamins and minerals
- does not use food from all food groups
- is energy dense
- contains additives
- expensive
- does not meet the dietary guidelines

Dinner menu

Dinner 1
Roast chicken
Broccoli, carrots
Potato
Gravy
Fresh fruit salad
Fromage frais

Dinner 2
Chicken nuggets
Potato waffles
Peas
Tomato sauce
Choc ice

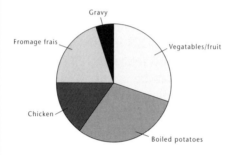

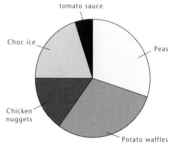

Advantages of dinner 1
Food groups
fruit and vegetables (broccoli, carrots, fresh fruit salad)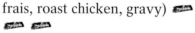
meat, fish and alternatives (chicken)
milk and dairy produce (fromage frais)
bread and cereals (potatoes)
fatty and sugary foods (fromage frais, roast chicken, gravy)

Advantages of dinner 2
Food groups
fruit and vegetables (peas)
meat, fish and alternatives (chicken)
milk and dairy produce (choc ice)
bread and cereals (potato waffles)
fatty and sugary foods (choc ice, potato waffles, chicken nuggets, tomato sauce)

Nutrition
protein (chicken, fromage frais)
carbohydrate (potatoes, gravy)
calcium (fromage frais)
iron (broccoli, chicken)
vitamin B (broccoli, fresh fruit, chicken)
vitamin C (fresh fruit, broccoli)
vitamin D (fromage frais)

Nutrition
protein (chicken, peas)
carbohydrate (potatoes, peas)
calcium (choc ice, peas)
iron (peas, chocolate)
vitamin A (peas)
vitamin B (peas, chocolate)

Dietary guidelines
low fat (chicken without the skin)
NSP (fruit and vegetables)
low sugar (natural fruit sugar)
low salt (salt naturally present)

Dietary guidelines
fat (high in nuggets, waffles and methods of cooking)
NSP (peas)
sugar (high in chocolate and tomato sauce)
salt (high in nuggets, peas, waffles, sauce and added salt)

Other advantages
- suitable for all age-groups
- colourful
- uses food from all food groups
- fresh fruit salad can be prepared in advance
- leftover chicken can be used for sandwiches
- chicken bones can be used for stock
- could suit any occasion

Other advantages
- quick and easy to prepare
- all pre-cooked
- no waste

Disadvantages of dinner 1
- expensive
- a lot of preparation
- uses a variety of cooking methods
- a lot of dishes to wash

Disadvantages of dinner 2
- expensive
- does not use food from all food groups
- does not meet dietary guidelines
- lacking in vitamins
- contains additives
- would only appeal to children and teenagers

KEY WORDS

balanced meal
breakfast
dietary guidelines
dinner
food groups
lunch
nutrition
planning meals

SUMMARY

- A well-balanced diet contains all the nutrients the body requires.
- Foods should be chosen following the dietary guidelines set out in *The Balance of Good Health*.
- Breakfast is an important start to the day.
- A daily diet is usually comprised of three main meals.

QUESTIONS

1 a Suggest six points which should be considered before planning a meal.

  b Choose two of these and explain each in detail.

2 Suggest a breakfast, lunch and dinner menu for one day. Record your menu in an illustrated format.

Planning menus for people with special dietary requirements

The most important consideration when planning meals is to meet the nutritional needs of all the individuals in the family.

The simplest way to provide well-balanced meals is to follow the guidelines set out in *The Balance of Good Health* (see Chapter 12).

Families differ in their dietary needs, one or more members of the family may have special dietary requirements brought about, for example, by one of the following conditions: pregnancy, heart disease, vegetarianism, food allergy, convalescent, weight problems.

Pregnancy in the family

When planning meals for the whole family the special needs of the pregnant woman must be taken into consideration.

Mother (6 months pregnant), father (manual worker in good health), with their two children aged 10 and 6 years.

Suggested meals for one day

Breakfast	Light meal	Main meal
fruit juice	toasted sandwich	shepherd's pie
muesli and banana	(cheese, ham and	carrots and
with semi-skimmed	tomato)	parsnips
milk	piece of fresh fruit	broccoli
wholemeal toast and	yoghurt	apple tart and
marmalade	herb tea	custard
herb tea		fruit juice

- these meals are planned to provide the nutrients required for a growing foetus and to maintain a healthy mother
- during pregnancy strong tea or coffee, highly seasoned and rich foods, and fatty foods should be avoided
- avoid snacking with energy-dense foods
- larger portions will satisfy the requirements of the other family members.

A vegetarian in the family

Mother (aged about 35 with part-time job), father (teacher), with their teenage daughter (lacto-vegetarian aged 16 years) and son aged 12 years.

Suggested meals for one day

Breakfast	**Light meal**	**Main meal**
grapefruit	veggieburger	vegetarian
boiled egg	(beefburger for	lasagne
wholemeal toast and	other family	mixed bean
marmalade	members)	salad
tea	coleslaw	baked potato
	milk	strawberry mousse

- nutritional needs of all the family members are met
- vegetarian needs have been considered without compromising the nutrients provided by animal flesh
- no need to cook separate meals for different members of the family.

Family with a heart disease sufferer

Mother (aged 45 years), father (aged 45 with coronary heart disease), with their 14 year old son and 17 year old daughter.

Suggested meals for one day

Breakfast	Light meal	Main meal
bran flakes and sliced banana with skimmed milk wholemeal toast small portion low fat spread tea (with skimmed milk)	wholemeal salad rolls with cottage cheese fresh fruit coffee (with skimmed milk)	grilled/baked white fish grilled tomato peas and sweetcorn boiled potatoes stewed fruit and natural yoghurt

- suitable for all family members
- fats have been kept to a minimum
- NSP (to give a feeling of fullness) has been increased using lots of fruit and vegetable and wholemeal products
- quantities can be reduced for those wishing to lose weight.

SUMMARY

- Meal planning should take account of any special dietary needs.
- Pregnant women need to eat well-balanced meals to maintain their own health and for the growth of the baby.
- Meals for vegetarians should be planned to include nutrients normally provided by animal foods.
- A diet low in animal fat and high in NSP is recommended for people suffering from heart disease.

KEY WORDS
heart disease
pregnancy
special dietary
  requirements
vegetarian

QUESTIONS

1 State four points to be considered when planning a meal for a family where the mother is pregnant.

2 Plan a packed lunch for a teenager who is lacto-vegetarian. Justify your choice of foods.

3 Evaluate the main meal given for a person with heart disease in the section above.

CHAPTER 18

Organization and meal preparation

The planning and cooking of a meal requires careful organization and timing. It is important to consider all the tasks which have to be completed so that all of the meal will be ready at a set time.

To do this efficiently, it is wise to devise a time plan which breaks down the tasks into logical steps.

When making a time plan the following points should be considered:

1 The time at which the meal is to be served.
2 The time required to prepare each dish.
3 The time required to cook each dish.
4 The time required to decorate, garnish or chill.

Dinner

MENU			
Shepherd's pie	**1**	Meal to be served at 6 pm	(1½ hours)
Broccoli			
Fruit juice (carton)		**2** Shepherd's pie	30 mins
Peach flan	Preparation time	Juice	2 mins
		Peach flan	20 mins
		Broccoli	2 mins
		3 Shepherd's pie	30 mins
	Cooking time	Broccoli	7 mins
		Peach flan	15 mins
		4 Garnish	5 mins

EQUIPMENT LIST

kettle
2 medium saucepans and lids
chopping board and knife
pot stand
measuring jug
potato peeler and masher
plate/bowl/sieve
flan tin
electric hand whisk
casserole dish
wooden spoon
fork/metal spoon

INGREDIENTS LIST

Shepherd's pie
500 g mince steak
2 carrots
1 onion
150 ml water
1 tablespoon flour
1 beef stock cube
1 dessertspoon Worcester sauce
8 potatoes
100 ml milk
25 g margarine
seasoning
1 tomato (to garnish)
sprig of parsley (to garnish)

Broccoli
4 portions of broccoli

Fresh fruit juice

Peach flan
2 large eggs
50 g caster sugar
50 g self-raising flour
1 large tin peaches
1 packet orange quick jel

TIME PLAN

Time	Tasks to be completed	Reminders
4.30–4.40	Collect equipment and ingredients. Grease and line flan tin. Grease casserole dish.	Put on oven 200 °C/Gas 6. Boil kettle.
4.40–4.50	Wash, peel and cut potatoes into quarters. Cook in boiling water 20–25 minutes approximately.	
4.50–5.00	Make sponge flan using whisking method: whisk eggs and sugar until creamy. Fold in flour using a metal spoon. Pour mixture into prepared flan tin. Bake in oven 15 minutes approximately.	
5.00–5.10	Chop onion, dice carrots. Brown mince in saucepan. Add onion, cook for a few minutes. Sprinkle in flour. Stir. Add carrots and stir in dissolved stock cube. Simmer 10 minutes.	Boil kettle. Dissolve stock cube. Check potatoes. Check flan.
5.10–5.25	Tidy table, wash dishes. Remove flan from oven. Cool on cooling tray. Drain potatoes, mash and cream. Put mince into casserole dish. Cover with creamed potatoes and decorate with a fork. Cook in oven 20–30 minutes until golden on top.	Turn up oven 220 °C/Gas 7.
5.25–5.35	Drain peaches. Blend quick jel with measured juice. Prepare garnishes. Wash dishes. Set table.	
5.35–5.40	Heat quick jel. Leave to cool. Arrange peaches in flan. Pour quick jel over peaches and leave to set on serving plate.	Boil kettle. Heat serving dish for broccoli.
5.40–5.50	Wash and prepare broccoli. Cook in boiling water 7–10 minutes approximately. Wash dishes.	Check pie. Check broccoli.
5.50–6.00	Remove pie from oven. Garnish with sliced tomato and parsley. Drain broccoli. Serve meal and drink.	Switch off cooker.

Snack

MENU

Ham, cheese and tomato toastie
Side salad
Tea

EQUIPMENT LIST		INGREDIENTS LIST

EQUIPMENT LIST	Toastie	Tea
sandwich toaster/grill	1 tomato (small)	tea or teabag(s)
grater	75 g low fat cheese	milk
chopping board	1 slice ham	sugar
chopping knife	2 slices wholemeal bread	
tea knife	low fat spread	
tea pot	salt and pepper	
serving plate		
kettle	Side salad	
bowl	lettuce	
	red pepper	
	cucumber	
	onion	
	ready-made coleslaw	

TIME PLAN		

Time	Tasks to be completed	Reminders
12.30–12.40	Collect equipment and ingredients. Set table.	Heat sandwich toaster/grill.
12.40–12.50	Grate cheese, wash and slice tomato, chop ham. Wash salad vegetables. Prepare side salad – shred lettuce, slice cucumber, onion and pepper.	Tidy table.
12.50–1.00	Butter one side of bread. Spread cheese, tomato and ham filling on unbuttered side of bread, season with salt and pepper. Place buttered slice on top (buttered side up) of filling. Place on toaster and close down lid firmly (or put under grill). Toast 2–3 minutes approximately. Wash dishes.	Boil kettle.
1.00	Make tea. Serve snack with side salad and coleslaw.	Switch off toaster/grill.

Food safety

It is important to be aware of **dangers** in the home, especially in the kitchen. Many accidents can be avoided if sensible care is taken when using equipment and preparing food.

Safety when preparing food

1 Be careful when using and washing sharp utensils, e.g. sharp knives and food processor blades.
2 Use oven gloves when checking and removing food from the oven.
3 Keep saucepan handles turned inwards on the cooker.
4 Mop up spills immediately to avoid falls.
5 Use good quality saucepans – well-balanced and with heat resistant handles. Make sure the handles are secure.
6 Take care with chip pans. Do not overfill or leave unattended.
7 Sweep up breakages and dispose of them carefully.
8 Look for BSI labels when purchasing small equipment.

Safety when using electrical equipment

1 Ensure that there are no trailing flexes. Replace frayed flexes.
2 Do not handle electrical appliances with wet hands.
3 Keep electrical appliances in good working order. Have large appliances regularly serviced.
4 Do not leave dishwashers or washing machines on at night or when the house is empty.
5 Do not overload electrical sockets. Avoid the use of adaptors.
6 Use correct fuses in appliances.
7 Switch off appliances after use and before cleaning.
8 Equipment purchased should display the approval label **BEAB**.

Small children should be supervised at all times when in the kitchen.

Hygiene in the kitchen

1 Use clean utensils.
2 Make sure work surfaces are clean before beginning work.
3 Tie hair back, remove rings, wash hands and put on a clean apron.
4 Do not use cracked dishes as the cracks harbour bacteria.
5 Keep food clean, cool and covered.
6 Use clean dish cloths and tea towels.
7 Have washing up water as hot as possible. Use rubber gloves.
8 Do not allow pets into the kitchen.
9 Empty and disinfect bins regularly.
10 Clean out kitchen cupboards regularly.
11 Defrost and clean fridge regularly. Keep fridge temperature below 5°C. Keep freezer temperature below −18°C.
12 Keep raw and cooked foods separate (in case of cross-contamination). Bacteria from raw meat can contaminate cooked meats which will not be cooked again before serving, hence the risk of **food poisoning**.
13 Do not use food past its 'use by' date.
14 Cover all cuts with a waterproof plaster.

Personal hygiene

- Do not touch face or hair when handling food
- Avoid coughing or sneezing over food
- Wash hands after using the toilet, before touching food and frequently during food preparation
- Do not smoke in food rooms

When handling food

- Use separate boards for raw and cooked foods
- Take care when handling high risk foods (e.g. raw meat, dairy produce, milk desserts, gravies, etc.)
- Take care when reheating foods
- DO not lick fingers

Storing food

- Store food in clean cupboards off the floor
- Store vegetables in a cool, dark area
- Keep pests out of the kitchen
- Keep food covered
- Store food at the correct temperature

SUMMARY

- It is important to be aware of the dangers in the home and to know how to avoid them.
- Care should be taken when preparing food and when using electrical equipment.
- Food can be contaminated by poor hygiene.
- Personal hygiene is essential when preparing and handling food.

KEY WORDS

dangers
food poisoning
hygiene
personal hygiene
safety

● ●

QUESTIONS

1 Suggest six points that will help prevent an outbreak of food poisoning when preparing food in the home.

Picture A

Picture B

2 Identify the dangers in Picture A.
Identify the unhygienic practices in Picture B.

3 Suggest how and where you would store the following foods to prevent food spoilage and contamination:

raw chicken	bananas
cooked ham	potatoes
bread	butter
cheese	milk
onions	an opened tin of beans.

110

Technology in the home

Technology has had an immense impact on the home. The development of advanced equipment and products has changed the home environment and improved the quality of life.

The development of technology has led to the provision of a huge variety of foods being made available for use throughout the year. Foods which are normally perishable can be processed, treated or packaged in such a way that:

- shelf life is increased
- micro-organisms are kept at a safe level
- ripening of food is delayed
- food waste is reduced
- quality of food is consistent
- colour and texture of food is improved
- foods are available out of season.

Storage equipment: Freezer

Foods

vegetables	bread
meats/burgers	cakes, buns, biscuits
desserts	fish
meals	ice cream
pastry	lollies

Advantages

- bacteria cannot multiply at −18°C
- can store foods that are surplus to immediate needs
- ready-made meals save time
- food can be stored for long periods
- food can be prepared in advance and stored
- nutrients are retained.

Disadvantages

- foods require lengthy defrosting time
- food cannot be refrozen unless it is cooked and cooled first
- food needs to be wrapped well to prevent damage and freezer burns
- food needs to be date stamped, labelled and used in rotation
- foods must be cool before being put in the freezer
- texture and flavour may deteriorate
- food should be stored only for the recommended time and according to the star rating (see Chapter 24).

Chilled/convenience foods

Foods
ready-made meals
cheese
eggs, milk
yoghurts, dairy
  products
desserts
garlic bread,
  sausage rolls
bacon, chicken
salad dishes

Advantages
- ready-made meals save time
- some foods are ready to eat or cook.

Disadvantages
- food may have been stored incorrectly and therefore be unsafe
- food must be eaten by 'use by' date
- food has a short shelf life.

Convenience foods are those which require little or no preparation.

The aims of convenience foods are to:
- supply a variety of foods, partly or completely prepared for the table
- maintain quality
- make foods attractive
- reduce preparation time
- provide for a range of family sizes (one, two or four people, or party packs)
- eliminate the need for sophisticated cooking skills.

Additives

Food **additives** can be grouped into four categories, according to whether they affect taste, texture, colour or **shelf life**.

Taste

| flavourings
flavour enhancers
sweeteners | **Effect**
● flavour of food is improved
● flavour which has been lost during processing is replaced
● flavour can be added or intensified. |

Texture

| emulsifiers
stabilizers
thickeners
anti-caking agents
gelling agents
raising agents | **Effect**
● prevents fats from separating
● foods are thickened, e.g. soups
● lumps are prevented from forming in powdery foods
● gels are added to make foods set, e.g. desserts
● foods rise, e.g. cakes. |

Colour (E100–E199)

| synthetic
natural | **Effect**
● food is made to look more attractive
● colour lost during processing is replaced. |

Shelf life

| preservatives
anti-oxidants | **Effect**
● spoilage is delayed
● prevents fats and oils going rancid. |

Nutrients

● added to fortify foods and replace nutrients lost.

Irradiation

Irradiation is a relatively new method of preservation. It kills bacteria, **micro-organisms**, enzymes and parasites and hence shelf life is prolonged.

Foods
potatoes
vegetables
tomatoes
strawberries
mushrooms
shellfish
prawns

Irradiation symbol

Advantages
- food looks and tastes as if it were fresh
- foods are safe to eat
- foods have a long shelf life.

Disadvantages
- food may not be labelled as irradiated, so consumers may be unaware that it has been irradiated
- vitamin C is destroyed
- food may be sold as fresh.

Packaging

Packaging is the protection used to hold food, keeping it safe and hygienic. It can be made from paper, plastic, metal or glass.

Paper packaging

Foods
eggs
milk
juice
butter
margarine

Plastic packaging

Foods
sauce
drink
margarine
bread
fruit
vegetables

Metal packaging

Foods
tinned foods
drinks
biscuits
pies

Glass packaging

Foods
milk
juice
mayonnaise
pickles
jam
beetroot
cook-in sauces
baby foods

Advantages
- provides protection from bacteria
- provides protection from damage
- prevents food losing moisture
- increases shelf life
- gives information, e.g. contents, cooking time, etc.
- easier to transport
- easier to handle and store
- makes product look more attractive
- prevents cross-contamination and transfer of flavours from one food to another
- vacuum packing can increase shelf life further
- spills are prevented
- can be cooked in the packaging
- some packaging can be recycled.

Disadvantages
- makes product more expensive
- packaging can be deceptive (small product – big pack)
- fruit and vegetables can be bruised
- glass can be heavy and is easily broken
- some packaging can react with food, e.g. tin
- cling film can react with high fat foods
- some packaging is not biodegradable.

Food processing

Technology has led to the development of products, processes and gadgets which make the preparation of meals effortless and less time-consuming.

There are a number of different **preservation processes** that are widely used.

Canning

Drying (dehydration)

Freezing

Cook/chill

Vacuum packing

SUMMARY

- Technology has had an immense impact on the home.
- A wide variety of foods is available all year round.
- Additives have many functions.
- Irradiation is widely used to preserve foods.
- Many different types of packaging are used in the food industry.
- Foods can be specially treated to prolong shelf life and simplify preparation.
- Convenience foods have made food preparation effortless and less time consuming.

KEY WORDS

additives
irradiation
micro-organisms
packaging
preservation process
shelf life
technology

QUESTIONS

1 What points should be considered when:
 a preparing fresh foods to be stored in the freezer
 b using food from the freezer?
2 Complete the following table:

Container	Food use	Packaging	Advantages	Disadvantages
bottle	milk	glass	recyclable	easily broken
cardboard carton				
polystyrene container				
tinfoil dish				
plastic bottle				
plastic bag				

3 What is food irradiation?
4 Discuss how technology has improved the quality and variety of foods available in the shops.

Labour-saving devices

Labour-saving equipment for the preparation of food has been designed either to make the preparation of food much easier or to speed up cooking time.

Labour-saving devices for preparing food

Food processor

chops	crumbs
chips	minces
grates	slices
juices	creams
purees	blends
whisks	

Features
- lockable lid
- pulse control button.

Points to consider
- care needs to be taken when washing metal blades
- parts may be difficult and awkward to wash
- some foods are easily over-processed, e.g. vegetables, fruit, etc.
- food pusher needs to be used to press food through when grating or slicing.

Electric mixer

creams	beats
whisks	whips
makes dough	mixes
kneads	

Features
- can opener, coffee grinder, potato peeler, liquidizer, juicer and mincer attachments can be added
- has varying speeds
- may be used as a hand mixer.

Points to consider
- larger mixers are unsuitable for small quantities
- small mixers are unsuitable for large quantities
- large mixers can be noisy
- some mixers may be dangerous when in use. They need to be switched off when adding ingredients or when cleaning the sides of the bowl
- some mixers are quite heavy.

Tin opener

opens tins
opens bottles

Points to consider
- essential, especially for the elderly, disabled and children
- easy to use
- safe
- no jagged edges
- difficult to clean.

Blender

whisks
crumbs
purees
chops
blends
mixes

Points to consider
- easy to use
- good for small quantities
- easy to wash
- lightweight
- safe to use
- no exposed sharp edges
- can be used on any container, saucepan, etc.

Liquidizer

blends
purees
crumbs
chops
grinds
whips

Points to consider
- may be bought freestanding or as an attachment
- must not be overfilled
- lid needs to be kept on when in use
- can be awkward to clean.

Labour-saving devices for cooking food

Electric wok

A **wok** is a large frying pan used for frying foods quickly. It is suitable for vegetables and small, tender pieces of meat.

Cooking in a wok is considered to be a healthy method of cooking because so little oil is used.

Multi-cooker

A **multi-cooker** is a deep frying pan with a lid. It can be used to fry, roast, steam, braise, bake and stew foods. It can be used as a small cooker (ideal if there are limited cooking facilities, e.g. in a bedsit). It can also be used as a griddle.

TEFLON-COATING

The wok and the multi-cooker may be teflon-coated, making them non-stick and easy to wash. They can be fully immersed in water. Plastic or wooden utensils must be used to avoid scratching the surface.

Pressure cooker

A **pressure cooker** is a large saucepan with a rubber-sealed locking lid. When the liquid in the saucepan is heated, steam builds up and the pressure inside the saucepan is increased. The temperature of the liquid is raised and therefore cooking time is reduced considerably.

There are different types of pressure cooker available, some depend on a pressure weight being used while others have a built-in cook control in the lid.

A complete meal can be cooked in one pot.

Cooking with a pressure cooker saves cooking time and fuel, retains flavours and nutrients, and reduces washing up. Tough cuts of meat can be made tender in a shorter time than when using traditional cooking methods.

Electric kettle

An **electric kettle** is used to boil water quickly. Models come in a kettle or a jug shape.

Electric jug kettle

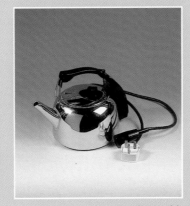

Traditional kettle

Jug kettles are economical as smaller quantities of water can be boiled using less electricity. Cordless models are available which are safer and easier to use, particularly for the elderly.

Features
- water-level gauge
- water filter
- automatic switch-off button
- safety cut-out device.

Electric toaster

An **electric toaster** toasts bread evenly and quickly. Different sizes and widths are available to suit different thicknesses of bread. The outside walls of the toaster are insulated so that they remain cool and therefore safe to touch.

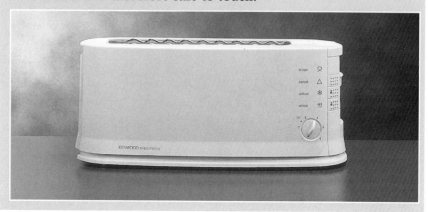

Features
- defrost setting
- reheat setting
- browning control
- pop-up action.

Sandwich toaster

A **sandwich toaster** consists of two thermostatically controlled, non-stick heating plates which are divided into two sections. Sandwiches are placed on the bottom plate. When the lid is closed the edges are sealed, the bread is toasted on both sides and the filling is heated.

They are useful for quick, snack meals and can be used anywhere where there is a power point.

Rice cooker

A **rice cooker** is a large, thermostatically controlled pot with an inner bowl and lid. A measuring cup is provided.

It can be used to steam vegetables and other foods as well as to cook rice.

Deep fat fryer

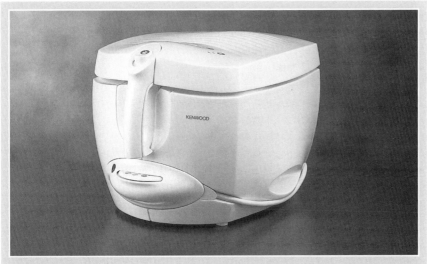

A **deep fat fryer** is a large, deep, thermostatically controlled pan with a removable frying basket and hinged lid which prevents splashing and reduces the risk of fire. To reduce odours and grease, a washable filter is fitted into the lid. The level of oil required in the pan is clearly marked. The temperature can be regulated to suit the cooking of different foods. It is suitable for cooking a wide range of foods safely.

Microwave oven

A **microwave oven** is a small oven. It radiates high frequency energy which causes the water molecules within the food to vibrate. This generates heat which cooks the food. The microwave oven cooks food quickly due to the high speed of vibrating molecules in the food. The oven remains cold throughout the cooking process, only the food becomes hot, although the food may, in turn, heat the cooking utensil by contact.

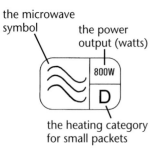

the microwave symbol

the power output (watts)

the heating category for small packets

Microwave labels can be found on ovens and food packs

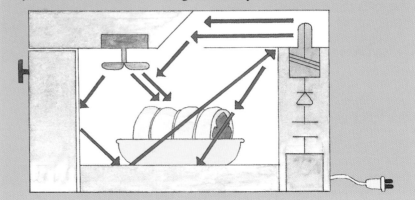

Advantages

- speeding up of cooking time (up to 75 percent), e.g. baked potatoes cook in about 4 minutes compared to 60 minutes in a conventional oven
- no pre-heating time required
- retains flavour, vitamins and colour
- uses less electricity, therefore economical
- easy to use and clean
- can be used anywhere where there is a power point
- saves washing up as foods can be cooked in the serving dish
- cuts down on cooking smells
- food can be cooked from frozen
- versatile – boils, bakes, roasts, stews, thaws, reheats and cooks
- safe for the elderly, disabled people and children as there are no hot surfaces
- useful for families with flexible meal times
- less wastage (cook only the amount of food required).

Disadvantages

- not suitable for large portions – takes longer to cook
- food does not brown or crisp
- cannot use metal utensils in oven
- does not cook food evenly, requires stirring
- requires 'standing time' i.e. food continues to cook after oven has switched off
- some foods are unsuitable
- easy to over cook – timing must be accurate.

Types of microwave ovens

● microwave – cooks with microwave only

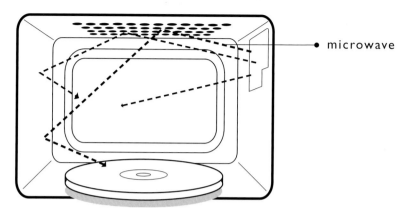

Microwaves are reflected by the metal sides of the oven and absorbed by the food.

● microwave with grill – cooks with microwave and browns top of food

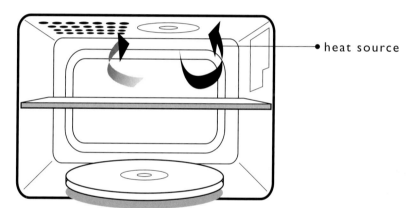

This is used to cook toast, steaks and other food that needs to be browned.

● **combination microwave** – can be used separately as a microwave, grill or oven, or as a combination

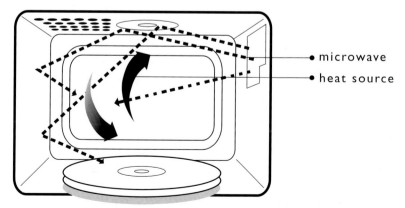

Conventional heat crisps the food and browns it. Microwaves reduce the cooking time.

Fan-assisted oven

Fan-assisted ovens have a heating element and a fan at the back of the oven. The fan circulates the heat evenly throughout the oven (unlike conventional ovens which are hotter at the top and cooler at the bottom).

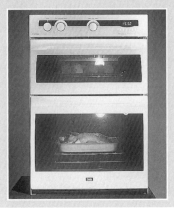

Advantages
- food cooks evenly on *all* shelves
- food can be placed near the heating element without burning
- cooking time may be less due to uniform cooking
- oven requires less heating up time and a lower temperature than a conventional oven
- easy to clean as there is less splashing
- ideal for batch baking
- four shelves as opposed to three in the conventional oven.

Halogen ceramic hob

A halogen ceramic hob gives instant heat. Halogen tubes combined with spiral heating elements provide precise control. The hob glows when heating. The hob needs to be cleaned and conditioned regularly to maintain condition. The correct type of saucepan must be used on halogen ceramic hobs to get good results.

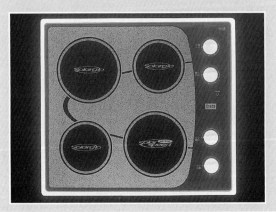

Advantages
- instant heat
- good contact with saucepan base provides good transmission of heat
- safe to use
- children do not get burnt (they can see when it is hot).

Twin grill

A twin grill enables the cook to use either half the grill or the whole grill when cooking.

Advantages
- saves energy
- gives flexibility when cooking.

SUMMARY

- Technological advances are continually influencing food preparation in the home.
- Labour-saving devices for preparing and cooking food save time and energy.
- A wide range of appliances are available for use in the kitchen.

KEY WORDS
blender
combination microwave
deep fat fryer
electric kettle
electric mixer
electric toaster
fan-assisted oven
food processor
halogen ceramic hob
labour-saving
liquidizer
microwave oven
multi-cooker
pressure cooker
rice cooker
sandwich toaster
tin opener
wok

QUESTIONS

1 Select four labour-saving devices which help a dual-earner family prepare healthy meals. Justify your choice.

2 Sue is weaning her four-month-old baby. Using the information below and in Chapter 21, choose the most suitable blender for her, giving reasons for your choice.

A • costs £25
  • has a jug which sits on the motor
  • assembles easily
  • can be difficult to remove small pieces of food
  • difficult to clean
  • jug may crack

B • costs £15
  • has a motor unit with a sharp blade at one end
  • portable
  • does not chop nuts, etc.
  • can be messy
  • sharp blades may be dangerous

3 A student on a limited budget has the following appliances: a microwave oven, a sandwich toaster and a multi-cooker. Assess the usefulness of these pieces of equipment and suggest two healthy dishes which could be prepared using each appliance.

SECTION 3
Choice and management
of resources

Factors which influence consumer choice

Consumer choice, the way people choose to spend their money, is influenced by many factors. Whilst people have some freedom of choice there are many factors which may affect their choice.

Personal factors

media
(techniques used to persuade people to buy)

fashion
(changing trends in clothes, music and food)

family, friends and other people
(upbringing influences habits and tastes in decision making)

wants
(something they could live without)

time
(labour-saving devices, convenience foods, time to shop around)

money
(how much they can afford)

emotions/mood
(how they feel e.g. buying an item to cheer themselves up)

needs
(essential items, e.g. food, clothes, etc.)

sense
(feelings of hunger, thirst, smell of cooking, etc.)

values
(what is personally important in life, e.g. car, holiday, house repairs etc.)

likes/dislikes
(personal taste or preferences)

Social factors

hobbies
(specialist equipment for hobbies e.g. fishing tackle, cycles)

entertainment
(holidays, CDs, magazines, clubs, discos)

gender
(females have different interests and needs from males, e.g. cosmetics)

age
(different age groups have different interests, therefore different wants, e.g. young adult–fast cars)

family
(likes and dislikes may be passed onto children)

friends
(teenagers in particular are influenced by their friends)

other people
(recommendations that help to make decisions)

trends
(things which are in vogue, e.g. healthy foods or keeping fit)

Economic factors

what they want or can afford

credit cards

mail order catalogues

special offers

value for money

reduced prices (sales)

income

Buy now Pay later (hire purchase)

savings stamps, air miles, loyalty cards, etc.

promotions

Psychological factors

celebrations
(money spent on special occasions,
e.g. Christmas, birthdays, anniversaries,
weddings)

advertisements
(shampoos, cosmetics, slimming aids, etc.
make people believe they will look better)

to bribe/encourage/reward
(e.g. children are often given gifts
when they do their best)

planned buying
(buying goods when all
options have been considered)

impulse buying
(buying something on the
spur of the moment)

emotions
(buying an item to make
themselves feel good)

Environmental factors

buying materials which can be reused
(fabric teatowels rather than paper towels,
terry nappies rather than disposables)

energy efficient products
(light bulbs, microwaves, thermostats,
lagging for pipes, etc.)

where they live
(smokeless zones – where
smokeless fuel should be used)

biodegradable packaging and detergents
(these break down into harmless
substances through natural processes)

Bottle
Bank

recyclable packaging
(aluminium cans, newspapers, plastic)

CFCs
(buying aerosols which are ozone friendly)

bottle banks
(bottles which can be recycled,
e.g. milk bottles instead of cartons)

lifestyle
(using less electricity or
other fuels in the home)

SUMMARY

- The way people spend their money is influenced by many factors.
- There are five main factors which influence consumer choice:
  personal, social, economic, psychological and environmental.

KEY WORDS
consumer choice
economic
environmental
personal
psychological
social

QUESTIONS

1 There are five main factors which influence consumer choice. List
these and give a simple explanation for each.

2 You have saved £120 to buy a CD system for your bedroom. List
all the factors which you would consider before making your
purchase.

3 In groups, discuss how families could help protect the
environment through their choice and use of goods and services
for their home.
Design a poster to illustrate your ideas.

Marketing strategies used to promote sales

Marketing is the management process which works out how to get the customers what they want when they want it efficiently and profitably. One part of marketing is the selling of the product. There are several ways to increase sales:

- advertising
- store promotions
- financial incentives
- store layout
- electronic and mail order shopping.

Advertising

Advertising is one way for manufacturers, retailers and consumers to communicate. It is a mechanism used to sell a product to the consumer by supplying a selected amount of information to encourage sales.

Forms of advertising

- newspaper adverts
- magazine adverts
- billboards/hoardings
- TV and radio adverts
- packaging/carrier bags/logos
- window displays
- sponsorships
- cinema
- public transport
- fliers/leaflets
- free samples.

Store promotions

Store promotions are used to encourage consumers to buy goods from a particular store or to try out new products.

Examples of store promotions

- free samples of products
- free tasting
- special offers
- buy one get one free
- loyalty cards/reward cards/ saving stamps
- own brands
- end-of-aisle displays
- cut-price sales
- loss leaders
- free gift.

LOST LEADERS

Products sold at a very low price to encourage people to shop in a particular store. Once inside the store the shoppers will hopefully buy more than just lost leaders.

Financial incentives

Money has a major influence on what people buy. All stores compete for business and many use **financial incentives** to entice people in.

Store layout

A lot of careful planning goes into the design and **layout** of goods within a store. Market research has shown that if goods are put in certain positions and displayed well, then consumers are encouraged to buy more:

- essentials (e.g. bread and milk) are usually placed at the back of the store so that customers have to walk past other tempting goods to get to them
- luxuries are placed at eye level; essentials on the lower shelves
- sweets and magazines are placed beside the checkout desk for impulse buying
- background music relaxes shoppers while they push the trolley around wide, spacious aisles
- smells around the fruit and vegetables and in the bread section tempt shoppers to buy
- colourful displays attract attention.

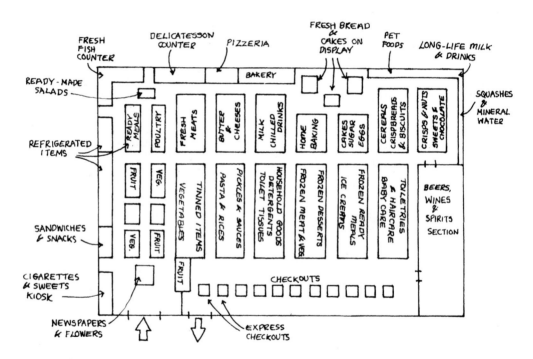

Electronic and mail order shopping

Technology has influenced the way in which we shop today. Computers:

- control stock
- order goods
- price goods
- read barcodes at the checkout desk
- enable the use of 'switch, credit and reward' cards at the checkout desk.

Electronic shopping benefits both retailer and the consumer as it:
- assists stock control
- eliminates human error
- cuts down on staffing
- indicates sales patterns
- saves time at checkouts
- makes the system more efficient
- provides a detailed receipt.

Mail order
Mail order shopping is very popular with people of all ages.

Advantages for the consumer
- items can be chosen in the comfort of their home
- convenient for those who live far from shops, the elderly, housebound and the disabled
- costs can be spread over weeks/months
- goods can be received on approval
- heavy items delivered direct to the home
- clothes can be tried on in the privacy of the home
- goods can be returned free of charge.

Disadvantages for the consumer
- encourages overspending
- it is difficult to judge the quality of goods
- tempting to buy unnecessary items
- encourages debt
- too easy to spend.

Shopping channel
A television **shopping channel** is an extension of mail order shopping. Products are advertised on television on a channel devoted to shopping. Goods can be selected and ordered by telephone. They are usually paid for by credit card. The products are delivered to the door.

KEY WORDS

advertising
electronic and mail
order shopping
financial incentives
store layout
store promotions
shopping channel

SUMMARY

- There are many marketing strategies designed to increase sales.
- Advertising can take many forms.
- Sales can be increased using special promotions.
- Financial incentives encourage people to spend money.
- Store layouts are designed to tempt the consumer to buy more.
- Computer technology is used for the benefit of the retailer and the consumer.
- Mail order shopping is a popular method of shopping for all ages.
- Using a television shopping channel is becoming a more widely used way of shopping.

QUESTIONS

1 List the advantages and disadvantages of buying a pair of jeans from a mail order catalogue.
2 Visit your local supermarket and list four marketing techniques used. Explain how successful each of these techniques is.
3 Look at the advertisements in this chapter and describe how these would influence the consumer.
4 Outline the way technology has changed shopping for:
   a the consumer
   b the retailer.

Consumer information

Consumer organizations

Consumer organizations are special bodies set up to inform and advise consumers.

The Consumers' Association

The Consumers' Association is the UK's largest independent not-for-profit consumer organisation and publishers of consumer magazines and books, including the monthly magazine called *Which?*. It campaigns to achieve improvements in goods and services for all customers, operating in the UK, EU and internationally.

    Which? provides the consumer with useful information on products and services. Each month it tests and reports on a selection of goods and services and may recommend a 'Best Buy'. Faults and dangers are highlighted to help prevent the consumer making expensive mistakes.

Consumers'
Association

Citizens Advice Bureau (CAB)

The Citizens Advice Bureau is an independent service which is free to the public. It provides confidential advice and guidance on many matters, e.g. personal, financial, consumer, employment and housing. There is an office in most large towns. Addresses can be found in the telephone directory.

Consumer Advice Centres

Consumer Advice Centres are operated by the local council and are often located close to shopping centres. They advise the consumer and the retailer on all aspects of buying and selling. The advice is free and they provide a range of booklets on consumer affairs.

The Office of Fair Trading (OFT)

The Office of Fair Trading is funded by the government. Its main function is to protect the consumer against unfair or misleading practices. It produces codes of practice which guarantee the quality of goods and acceptable standards of service. Booklets and pamphlets are published to guide the consumer on certain products and practices.

Trading Standards Department

The Trading Standards Department is a body set up to investigate false or misleading claims, descriptions or prices, inaccurate weights or measures and the safety of goods. It also helps to enforce legislation.

Environmental Health Department

The Environmental Health Department is authorized by the local authority to enforce health and safety and food legislation, and it deals specifically with health matters in relation to food and drink that is unfit for consumption. Food premises can be inspected at any time without prior notice, to try and maintain high standards and to ensure public safety.

Media

When information needs to be communicated to large numbers of people, several **media** can be used. Their aim is to inform, to educate, and to entertain.

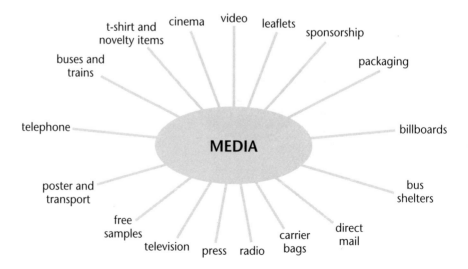

Television is probably the most powerful medium and has more influence than any other method of communication as it is widely viewed by people from all age-groups.

Labelling

Labels provide the consumer with valuable information. They are attached to a wide range of goods.

Care labels

Care labels, usually found on fabric items, advise on care.

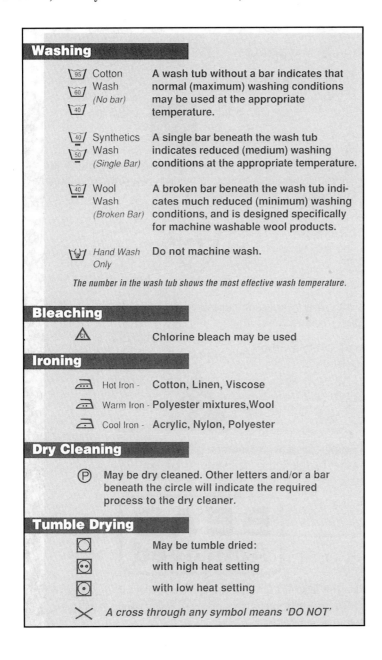

Washing

Cotton Wash *(No bar)* — A wash tub without a bar indicates that normal (maximum) washing conditions may be used at the appropriate temperature.

Synthetics Wash *(Single Bar)* — A single bar beneath the wash tub indicates reduced (medium) washing conditions at the appropriate temperature.

Wool Wash *(Broken Bar)* — A broken bar beneath the wash tub indicates much reduced (minimum) washing conditions, and is designed specifically for machine washable wool products.

Hand Wash Only — Do not machine wash.

The number in the wash tub shows the most effective wash temperature.

Bleaching

Chlorine bleach may be used

Ironing

Hot Iron - Cotton, Linen, Viscose

Warm Iron - Polyester mixtures, Wool

Cool Iron - Acrylic, Nylon, Polyester

Dry Cleaning

May be dry cleaned. Other letters and/or a bar beneath the circle will indicate the required process to the dry cleaner.

Tumble Drying

May be tumble dried:

with high heat setting

with low heat setting

A cross through any symbol means 'DO NOT'

Barcodes

Barcodes are found on many products. They are an important part of the electronic systems used in shops. A barcode records information on the product, usually relating to price, a description of the product and country of origin. A barcode can be read by a laser scanner.

Seals of approval and quality marks

Seals of approval and quality marks indicate that a product has passed certain tests for design, performance, reliability and safety. Here are some examples:

Examples of quality marks

Design Council – the Millennium Products label is found on British products which the Design Council has chosen as being forward-thinking, creative products and services

Kitemark – this label is found on household items which conform to standards set by the British Standards Institution

Examples of safety symbols

BSI Safety Mark – this label is found on gas and electric fittings which have passed tests set by the British Standards Institution. The manufacturer submits the item for testing

BEAB Mark – this label is found on domestic and electric appliances which have undergone British Electrotechnical Approvals Board safety tests to meet European and International standards

Safety/warning labels – this particular label advises the consumer that the upholstery is flame resistant

RESISTANT

Food labelling

Regulations (Northern Ireland) 1996

The Food Safety Order requires by law that all packaged food must be labelled. The law states that labels must include the following information:

- the name of the food
- ingredients (listed in descending order of weight)
- storage instructions
- shelf life ('use by' and 'best-before date')
- instructions for use
- quantity or net weight
- name and address of manufacturer, packer or EU seller.

Examples of other food labels

Suitable for vegetarians

Irradiation symbol – this symbol advises that the food has been irradiated

Freezing instructions – if the product can be frozen, this symbol is shown on the label with instructions

Microwave symbol – this symbol shows that food is microwavable, it is usually accompanied by cooking instructions

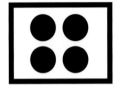 

Cooking instructions – manufacturers use different symbols to show how food can be cooked. These symbols show that the food can be cooked in an oven, on a hob, grill or a barbecue

Star marking – star markings are used by the manufacturers of fridges, freezers and frozen foods to describe how long food can be kept and at what temperature
1 star = −6 °C. Will store frozen food for one week.
2 stars = −12°C. Will store frozen food for one month.
3 stars = −18°C. Will store frozen food for three months.
4 stars = −18°C to −25°C. Deep freezer will freeze fresh food and store frozen food for up to 12 months.

Litterman symbol – this symbol is used to encourage people to dispose of their litter properly. It is most frequently used on snack foods such as crisps and cans of drink

Recycled symbol – this symbol indicates that recycled material has been used in the packaging

SUMMARY

- Consumer organizations have been set up to help, advise and protect the consumer and the retailer.
- The purpose of the media is to inform, educate and entertain the consumer.
- Labels provide the consumer with information for the use and care of products.
- Legally, all packaged foods must be labelled with certain information.

KEY WORDS
consumer
organizations
labels
media

* *

QUESTIONS

1 Draw two quality marks and two safety symbols. For each one, explain what they mean and give an example of where they might be displayed.

2 Explain the care instructions found on this clothing label.

3 British law states that food labels must contain certain information. Look at the label below. Identify the missing information.

4 Which consumer organization would you approach to obtain advice in each of the following situations:
   a you find broken glass in a jar of marmalade
   b you buy a leather jacket which you discover is made of plastic
   c you need advice on a debt problem
   d you need guidance in the purchase of a dishwasher?

5 Analyse three of the most effective strategies used by manufacturers to sell their products.

Legislation

Food Safety (Northern Ireland) Order 1991

The **Food Safety (Northern Ireland) Order 1991** applies to every link in the food chain from the origin of the food through to its sale. It includes people working in any aspect of food handling. It is an offence to sell any food which fails to meet safety requirements.

It is an offence to:

1 Serve food that has been made harmful by the addition or removal of certain substances.
2 Serve food that is unfit to eat.
3 Serve food that is so contaminated that it would be unreasonable to expect people to eat it.
4 Describe the nature of food inaccurately, e.g. sell stewing meat as sirloin.
5 Change the substance of food, e.g. sell watered-down whisky in a bar or hotel.
6 Change the quality of food, e.g. sell a meal that contains unwanted foreign matter such as a fly.

This applies to both major retailers and small restaurants, cafes and to any food sales, e.g. those at charity fund raising events.

The Environmental Health Department officers are authorized by the local authority to enforce this legislation.

Food Safety (General and Food Hygiene) Regulations (Northern Ireland) 1996

The food hygiene regulations are intended to ensure the hygienic operation of food premises.

- Food must be protected from contamination.
- Food must be stored and handled at safe temperatures.
- Food premises must have adequate hot/cold water supply.
- Separate hand washing facilities must be made available.
- Accommodation for outdoor clothing must be made available.
- Smoking in food preparation rooms is illegal.
- All cuts must be kept clean and covered with blue, waterproof dressings.
- Food handlers must wear suitable protective clothing.
- Food handlers must report to their supervisors if they suspect they are suffering from food poisoning.
- Food rooms must have satisfactory lighting and ventilation.
- First aid kits must be provided in all food rooms.
- Food rooms/equipment must be kept clean and in good condition.
- Waste must be disposed of well away from food rooms.

- All staff must be trained to appropriate level (depending on the job requirements).
- All food premises must have hazard analysis systems.

These regulations apply to any premises where food is handled. Environmental Health Department officers are empowered by the local authority to enforce these regulations.

Consumer Protection Act 1987

The **Consumer Protection Act 1987** requires that consumer goods are *safe*:
- it prohibits the supply of unsafe goods, demanding their removal from sale
- it sets safety standards for manufacturers to follow
- it requires the retailer/manufacturer to inform consumers of faults in items they may have purchased, e.g. cookers
- it prohibits misleading information about prices.

The Consumer Credit Act 1974

The purpose of the **Consumer Credit Act 1974** is to protect the consumer when buying on credit. The act covers most forms of credit including cash loans, credit sales and hire purchase.

Weights and Measures Act 1985

The **Weights and Measures Act 1985** controls the equipment used by manufacturers to weigh and measure goods. It aims to ensure the accuracy of quantities sold. Shops, markets, etc. can be checked regularly. Goods must be labelled accurately using metric measurements.

Trades Description Act 1968

The **Trades Description Act 1968** declares that goods must not be described in a false or misleading way and that any claim made about the item/goods/services must be accurate, e.g. if a jacket is described as waterproof it must repel rain/water.

Sale and Supply of Goods Act 1994

The **Sale and Supply of Goods Act 1994** states that all goods must be:
- as described, i.e. no false or exaggerated claims
- of satisfactory quality, of good working order, undamaged, of satisfactory appearance, safe, durable and well finished
- fit for their intended purpose, e.g. a hairdryer should dry hair.

This act also applies to all goods bought in sales, street markets, by mail order and from door-to-door salesmen, as well as to those bought in stores.

Trademark 1994

It is a criminal offence for any person to sell a Trademark that is not authentic (genuine). A Trademark needs to be registered in the Trademark Register. It then becomes a public document and is renewable every ten years. The Trademark Register lists each trademark stating:

- what it is
- what it looks like
- what category it is used for.

The Trademark is enforced by Trading Standards Department and the police.

Consumer complaints

If goods are faulty or not fit for their purpose, a consumer is entitled to complain.

How to make a complaint

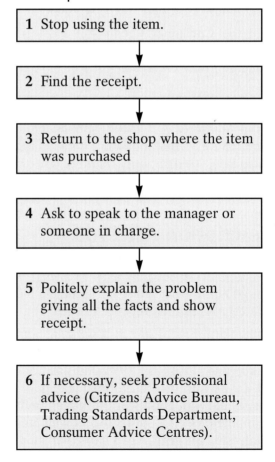

1 Stop using the item.

2 Find the receipt.

3 Return to the shop where the item was purchased

4 Ask to speak to the manager or someone in charge.

5 Politely explain the problem giving all the facts and show receipt.

6 If necessary, seek professional advice (Citizens Advice Bureau, Trading Standards Department, Consumer Advice Centres).

A consumer may seek compensation and may be entitled to a full refund.

SUMMARY

- Legislation is provided to protect the consumer.
- Food hygiene regulations are very strict.
- Legislation is enforced by the relevant government body and the police.
- Consumers have rights and should know how to make a complaint.

• •

QUESTIONS

1 Explain how the Food Safety (Northern Ireland) Order 1991 protects the consumer.

2 There are laws which protect the consumer. Consider the following situation. You have bought a waterproof jacket and it lets in water. What steps would you take and what outcome would you expect?

3 What are the implications of the Food Safety (General Food Hygiene) Regulations (Northern Ireland) 1996 for the manager of a restaurant?

KEY WORDS

Consumer Credit Act 1974

Consumer Protection Act 1987

Food Safety (General and Food Hygiene) Regulations (Northern Ireland) 1996

Food Safety (Northern Ireland) Order 1991

Sale and Supply of Goods Act 1994

Trademark 1994

Trades Description Act 1968

Weights and Measures Act 1985

CHAPTER 26

Choice of home

The **needs** of families and individuals change as they grow up and grow older. When a young person leaves home to study or to find a job, he/she may decide to rent a home or share accommodation with friends. As he/she grows older and jobs are secured, some may wish to invest in a home of their own. If they go on to have children they may need a larger home with garden space.

Although a person's needs may change according to circumstances, a home should provide the basic **physical**, **social** and **emotional** needs essential for a person's wellbeing:

- **shelter** from the elements
- warmth
- safety and security
- privacy
- a place to meet family and friends
- a familiar place in which a person feels comfortable and which provides a sense of belonging.

Factors to consider

Choosing a home is an important step. Many factors need to be considered as the choice could have long-term implications.

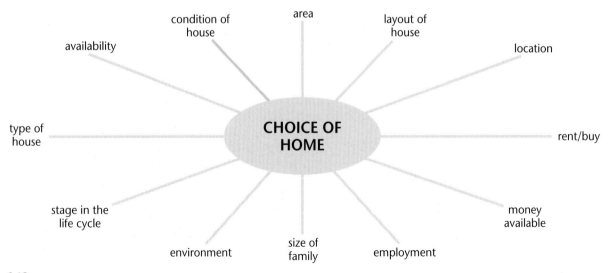

1 Condition of the house
- does it require major/minor alterations?
- is it furnished/unfurnished?
- does it need redecorating?

2 Availability
- is there a suitable house for sale/rent in the chosen area?

3 Stage in the life cycle
- single person – small, near to work
- student – low running costs, extra bedrooms to accommodate several people, easy to clean
- young couple with no children – near to work
- family with small children – garden, space, extra bedrooms, more than one toilet, etc.
- disabled/elderly – small, all on one level, low maintenance, suitable for adjustments to fittings.

4 Money available
- rent or buy
- size of home required.

5 Size of family
- larger families need larger homes.

6 Location
- near schools, work, shops, health centre, public transport, parks, playgrounds, leisure amenities, etc.

7 Type of house
- bungalow
- detached
- semi-detached
- sheltered accommodation/folds
- terraced
- modern
- old
- apartment
- flats
- mobile home.

8 Layout of house
- open plan
- conventional
- sufficient bedrooms
- well-planned kitchen
- upstairs and downstairs toilet.

9 Rent/buy
- short- or long-term home
- secure income
- investment
- ready to settle down.

10 Area
- rural/urban
- large/small estate
- new/mature area
- near relatives
- near other friends/families
- local services (doctors, library)
- local amenities (playgrounds, leisure centres)
- neighbours.

11 Employment
- near workplace – saving on travel cost and time
- convenience.

12 Environment
- main roads
- pollution (noise, smells)
- airport
- electricity pylons
- factories
- silage dumps
- derelict sites
- rubbish
- railway lines
- greenbelt
- countryside.

Economic factors

One of the main considerations when choosing a home is the finance available. People must consider what they can afford. **Economic** factors will influence the decision to opt for **renting** or for **home ownership**.

Renting a home

A person may decide to rent for one or more of the following reasons:

1 He/she is a student, requiring temporary accommodation.
2 He/she is working away from home.
3 He/she wishes to spend money in other ways, e.g. holidays.
4 He/she is a single parent.
5 He/she is on a low income, and would find it difficult to raise the deposit necessary to buy a home.
6 He/she has an insecure job.
7 He/she is jobless, depending on the State for benefits.
8 There is no suitable property available.
9 He/she wants to be able to move easily at short notice.

Advantages of renting

- no responsibility for upkeep
- no legal expenses
- no large deposit required
- easy to move at short notice
- the State may pay the rent.

Disadvantages of renting

- cannot make building alterations
- no return on rent money
- may be a limited number of houses available
- private landlords can increase the rent
- can be given short notice to leave
- may not allow pets/children.

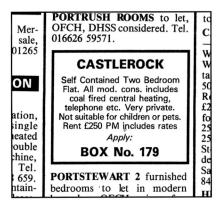

PORTRUSH ROOMS to let, OFCH, DHSS considered. Tel. 016626 59571.

CASTLEROCK

Self Contained Two Bedroom Flat. All mod. cons. includes coal fired central heating, telephone etc. Very private. Not suitable for children or pets. Rent £250 PM includes rates

Apply:

BOX No. 179

PORTSTEWART 2 furnished bedrooms to let in modern

Buying a home

Buying a home is usually considered to be an investment as the property would normally increase in value over the years.

Advantages of buying

- it is an investment
- it provides security
- structural alterations can be made
- tax relief on the cost may be available.

Disadvantages of buying

- large deposit needed
- legal expenses to be paid
- the owner is responsible for maintaining the property
- ground rent may be payable as well
- it may cost more than anticipated (e.g. interest rates may rise).

Ways to buy a home

There are different ways to buy a home. Most people borrow money from a bank or a building society. The loan is called a **mortgage** and it is repaid over a period of time (usually 25 years). An initial deposit of 5–10 percent of the value of the property must be paid. The balance of the money required is usually made up of a mortgage and/or the buyer's savings.

The two most common types of mortgage are:
- repayment mortgage
- **endowment** mortgage.

REPAYMENT MORTGAGE

The loan is paid off over a set term (usually 25 years) in monthly instalments. With each instalment some of the capital sum (the amount borrowed) and the interest due on it is paid back. The person taking out the mortgage must take out insurance cover, so that in the event of their death, the mortgage is fully paid off. This insurance increases the mortgage repayments. At the end of the term the buyer has paid off the debt.

ENDOWMENT MORTGAGE

Over a set term (usually 25 years) the interest on the capital sum (amount borrowed) is paid to the lender. At the same time, the buyer pays monthly instalments into an endowment saving scheme. At the end of the term, the amount of money paid into the scheme should have grown large enough to pay off the capital sum as well as to pay the buyer a lump sum. Endowment policies usually provide built-in life insurance so that if the buyer dies prematurely, the capital sum is paid off automatically. The disadvantage is that the endowment saving scheme may not build up enough money to pay back the capital sum.

Housing associations

Housing associations are non-profit making organizations, funded by the government, which provide homes for people who wish to buy a home but who cannot afford a full mortgage. They also rent properties to specific groups, e.g. elderly people or single people, who do not qualify for local authority housing.

The purpose of these associations is to provide low-cost home ownership schemes to help those who could not otherwise afford to buy.

Schemes

Co-ownership (shared ownership) scheme

A **co-ownership** scheme is for people who cannot afford to buy a home outright. A share of the property is bought and rent is paid on the remainder. This makes the monthly payment less. Further shares in the property may be bought if financial circumstances change.

Leasehold scheme

A **leasehold** scheme enables the elderly to buy a sheltered home, usually at 70 percent of the normal cost.

Running costs of the home

When choosing a home it is wise to budget for other costs as well as mortgage repayments or rent. Some of these other expenses will involve the **running costs**, which can use up to 20 percent of the family income.

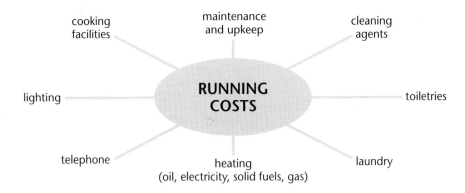

As the pie chart shows, the running costs of the home make up only part of the overall budget.

The percentage of the budget allotted to each expense may vary according to individual family needs.

Savings can be made if attention is paid to wastage.

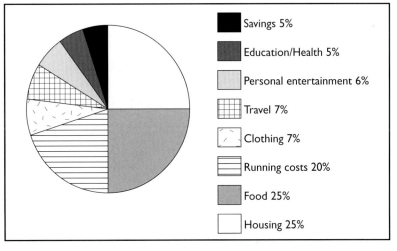

Savings 5%

Education/Health 5%

Personal entertainment 6%

Travel 7%

Clothing 7%

Running costs 20%

Food 25%

Housing 25%

KEY WORDS

co-ownership
economic
emotional
endowment
leasehold
mortgage
needs
ownership
physical
renting
running costs
shelter
social

SUMMARY

- A person's housing needs change as he/she progresses through the life cycle.
- The home should provide the basic needs for human wellbeing.
- Physical, social, emotional and economic factors influence a person's choice of home.
- The finance available is a major consideration when choosing a home.
- There are many ways to pay for a home.
- Running costs can use up to 20 percent of the budget.

● ●

QUESTIONS

1 List the basic needs that a home should provide.

2 What considerations should a couple with three children take into account when choosing a home?

3 Compare the advantages and disadvantages of renting and buying a home for a young, married couple who both have fairly secure jobs.

4 What is a mortgage?
Describe the two most common mortgages offered.

5 What options (other than a mortgage) are available to people who wish to purchase their own home? Indicate the conditions attached to these.

6 A family has a monthly income of £1000. Using the pie chart on page 153, suggest how this money should be allocated. Give figures.

Family finance

For most families money is a limited resource, therefore care should be taken when deciding how to spend it.

Few people can buy everything they want, so it is wise to **prioritize**. Essential items must be bought before non-essential items. Different families have different needs and priorities, but certain basic needs such as food, warmth, clothing and shelter must always be catered for.

The best way to decide how much money can be spent is to plan spending. This is called **budgeting** and it is the responsibility of the adult members of the family.

The purpose of a budget is to ensure that expenditure does not exceed income.

Income is the total amount of money coming into the home from benefits, earnings, savings and investments.

Expenditure is the total amount of money spent.

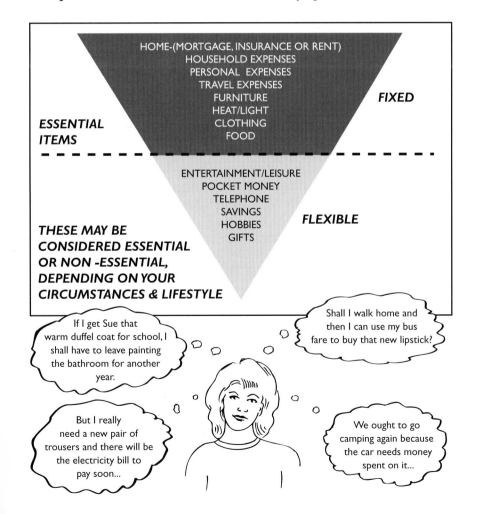

<table>
<tr><td colspan="2">HOME-(MORTGAGE, INSURANCE OR RENT)</td></tr>
</table>

HOME-(MORTGAGE, INSURANCE OR RENT)
HOUSEHOLD EXPENSES
PERSONAL EXPENSES
TRAVEL EXPENSES
FURNITURE
HEAT/LIGHT
CLOTHING
FOOD

FIXED

ESSENTIAL ITEMS

ENTERTAINMENT/LEISURE
POCKET MONEY
TELEPHONE
SAVINGS
HOBBIES
GIFTS

FLEXIBLE

THESE MAY BE CONSIDERED ESSENTIAL OR NON -ESSENTIAL, DEPENDING ON YOUR CIRCUMSTANCES & LIFESTYLE

If I get Sue that warm duffel coat for school, I shall have to leave painting the bathroom for another year.

Shall I walk home and then I can use my bus fare to buy that new lipstick?

But I really need a new pair of trousers and there will be the electricity bill to pay soon...

We ought to go camping again because the car needs money spent on it...

Budgeting

Here is an example of a budget for a family of four with a monthly income of £300.

Income	£300
Food (25%)	£75
Housing (25%)	£75
Household expenses (20%)	£60
Clothing (7%)	£21
Travel (7%)	£21
Health/personal expenses (5%)	£15
Entertainment (6%)	£18
Savings (5%)	£15
Total	£300

Living on a low income

Many families have a constant struggle to make ends meet. Those on a low income may qualify for some of the following benefits:

- family income support
- family credit
- housing benefit
- social fund
- cold weather payments.

Because the income is low, the *percentage* allocation of money to each item on the list differs to ensure that enough money is set aside to meet basic needs.

	Income £100	£150
Food (30%)	£30	£45
Housing (20%)	£20	£30
Household expenses (20%)	£20	£30
Clothing (10%)	£10	£15
Travel (10%)	£10	£15
Miscellaneous (to include personal and health) (10%)	£10	£15
Entertainment/savings (—)	(—)	(—)
Total	£100	£150

Methods of payment for goods and services

People pay for goods and services in a number of different ways.

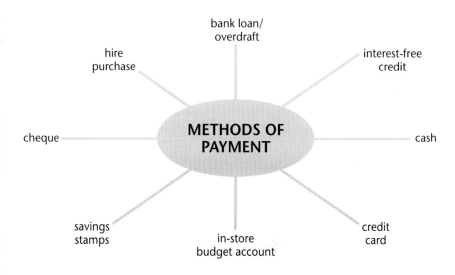

Cash
Coins and notes are exchanged for goods and services. This is called **cash**.

Cheques
A **cheque** is an official slip detailing an amount to be paid in exchange for goods and services. The sum of money is taken from the consumer's account in a bank or building society.

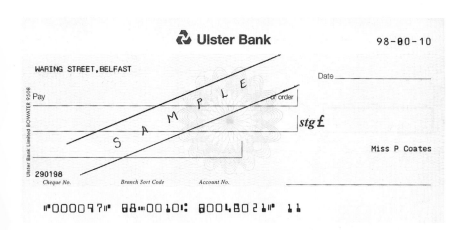

Saving stamps

Buying **saving stamps** can be a good way of ensuring that enough money is put aside to pay bills. The stamps can be accumulated and used along with cash to pay bills. They help avoid the need to suddenly find a large amount of money to pay a bill when it arrives.

There are many different types of saving stamps:

- telephone – £2 and £5 stamps
- television licence – £1 and £2 stamps
- gas – £2 stamps
- vehicle licence – £5 stamps.

Northern Ireland Electricity issue an *EasySaver* card. It has to be ordered two weeks in advance. Using *EasySaver*, money can be saved towards your electricity bill at *PayPoint outlets*, post offices and *Shop Electric* shops.

These are all methods of saving money regularly to help pay quarterly bills.

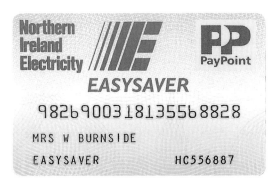

Credit cards

A **credit card** allows consumers to buy goods and services without the need for cash. There are many different credit cards. Consumers must satisfy certain requirements before they will be issued with a card. Each consumer has a credit limit. Payment is made to the credit card company on receipt of a monthly statement. Interest is added to unpaid accounts.

Hire purchase

Consumers use **hire purchase** to buy expensive items which they could not afford to pay for outright, e.g. a car. They pay a down payment on the goods and the balance is paid over several months. There is an additional charge for this service. The finance company owns the item until payments have been completed.

Interest-free credit

Some large stores offer interest-free credit on goods bought. Items purchased are paid for over several months. No interest is paid on the money owed unless consumers do not pay within the term agreed.

In-store budget account

Various retail outlets offer budget or store cards. These allow consumers to buy goods from the store, paying on receipt of a monthly statement. Customers can choose to take advantage of the card's credit facility, for which they will be charged a fixed rate of interest on the outstanding balance each month.

Bank loan

A bank loan is granted to consumers who have made special arrangements with the bank. Monthly repayments are made and interest is charged on the balance of the money owed.

Overdraft

An overdraft facility can be arranged with the consumer's bank. It allows consumers to take out more money than they have in their account, up to an agreed amount. Interest is usually payable on money overdrawn. Some banks will agree a modest overdraft limit on which no interest is payable. This is useful in avoiding unnecessary debt because of short-term problems, e.g. wages being paid late.

Electronic banking

In recent years the rapid advances in computer technology have made the access and use of money much easier and more convenient.

Cash cards

Cash cards are plastic cards containing a magnetic strip which holds the consumer's PIN (personal identification number). It allows the consumers to withdraw money from their bank or building society account using an Automated Telling Machine.

These machines can be found outside banks and at supermarkets, shopping centres, filling stations and other public places.

Debit cards

Debit cards allow consumers to pay for goods using funds transferred directly from their bank account to the store's account – but only if there is enough money in the account.

Barcode

Barcodes are found on products and their packaging. The code gives certain information about the product. As a checkout desk operator passes the product through a laser scan, the price is retrieved from a computer file and displayed on the till for the customer to see. The name of the product and the price is printed on the receipt.

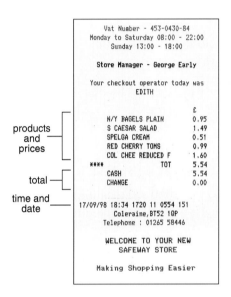

SUMMARY

- Money is a limited resource.
- Families need to prioritize.
- A plan of spending is called a budget.
- Families on low income may qualify for financial support from the government.
- Consumers can pay for goods and services in different ways.
- Credit is widely available.
- Technology has changed the way in which we access money today.

QUESTIONS

1 What are the main considerations to be taken into account when planning a budget for a young couple who have just purchased their first home?

2 A family with two children has a limited income.

a Suggest ways they could reduce household expenses.

b They need a new washing machine. Suggest alternative ways they could buy one.

3 Evaluate two of the methods of payment you have identified.

4 Identify each of the cards below and explain how they are used.

CHAPTER 28

Mismanagement of finances and possible consequences

Debt is a serious social problem which can lead to stress within the family. Many families get into financial difficulties because they fail to control their spending.

How debt occurs

1 Overspending.
2 Taking advantage of too many credit offers.
3 Ignoring bills.
4 Living beyond one's means.
5 'Keeping up with the Jones'.
6 Buying items on impulse, or buying non-essentials.
7 Poor budgeting.
8 Lack of savings for emergencies.
9 Using credit cards without paying them off.
10 Not facing up to debts.
11 Sudden drop in income.
12 Taking on too many financial commitments.

PROBLEMS INCURRED BY DEBT	
shame	physical illness
suicide	neglect
anxiety	loneliness
tension	poverty
breakdown of trust	loss of home and possessions

Debt advice

When a family finds themselves in debt they can seek **advice** from the Citizens Advice Bureau or the Money Advice Centre. Some companies such as Northern Ireland Electric, telephone companies or building societies will help people to plan repayments.

Management of debt

A combination of the **tactics** listed below could be used to find an appropriate strategy to deal with debt.

- seek help as soon as possible
- do not be tempted to take out a further loan to repay a debt
- do not ignore bills – discuss problems with the creditor
- do not be tempted to use a money lender
- examine the budget to identify where savings can be made
- use saving stamps
- economize in the home, e.g. switch off unnecessary lights, use fewer convenience foods
- request the instalment of a pay-as-you-use electricity meter
- investigate entitlement to benefits
- set a realistic target for repayment of debt
- arrange to have bills staggered
- arrange direct debits and budget for payments in monthly instalments.

Do not despair – debt problems can be solved.

KEY WORDS
advice
debt
management
strategies
tactics

SUMMARY

- Debt is a serious social problem.
- People can get into debt in many ways.
- Debt can cause personal and other family problems.
- Debt advice is available.
- Debt can be managed and problems can be solved.

QUESTIONS

> Mr and Mrs Smith and their three children live in a rented home. Mr Smith is a mechanic and earns £250 per week. Mrs Smith has a part-time job in the local shop and earns £40 per week.
>
>   They have just bought a new three-piece suite from a mail order catalogue. Mr Smith has taken up a special deal on a new car.
>
>   One of the children needs to pay the balance of £150 for a school trip to France.
>
>   The weekly food bill is £100.
>
>   The telephone and electricity bills are due.
>
>   They have used up most of their savings on a family holiday and now their cooker has stopped working.

1 Outline the consequences of the Smith's management of their finances.

2 Identify reasons why their debt has accumulated.

3 Suggest how the Smiths could solve their problem.

Management of resources

Management

Effective **management** involves thinking ahead, **planning**, monitoring and **evaluating** if the home is to be managed properly, its **resources** must be used efficiently.

Resources include:
- people – their time, energy, knowledge and skills
- products – food, equipment, fuel, utensils
- money – a means of purchasing resources.
- resources outside the home such as library, hospital, schools, local government, voluntary services.

Task management

The process required to carry out an individual task effectively involves five logical steps.

Applying the management process

Goal
- to tidy and clean the bedroom.

Resources
- time
- energy
- cleaning products
- vacuum cleaner.

Plan
- decide what tasks need to be carried out
- prioritize each task.

Action
- replace books on shelves
- hang up clothes
- put away CDs
- return dirty dishes and laundry to kitchen
- put shoes and other items away
- close drawers
- open window
- tie back curtains
- make bed
- dust
- vacuum.

Evaluation
- assess how well the job was carried out
- could it have been done any better, or in a different way?
- would you do it the same the next time or differently?

Technology in the home

There is a lot of sophisticated equipment available which makes household tasks easier and less time-consuming. Many items which were once luxuries are now considered to be essential for day-to-day living. Members of the family have more time to spend together and to pursue individual hobbies.

Technology in the kitchen

- housework less time-consuming
- less preparation required for food
- cleaning easier
- meals made more quickly
- fuel saved
- equipment easier to use.

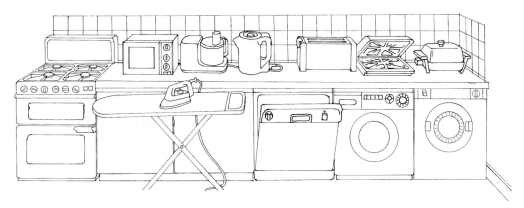

Technology in the living room/study

- relaxation easier
- information easier to access
- entertainment in the home
- presentation of work improved
- organization of household filing, budgeting and accounts improved
- communication with other people improved.

KEY WORDS

action
evaluate
goals
management
planning
resources
technology

SUMMARY

- Effective management involves careful planning.
- Resources must be used efficiently.
- Effective management involves logical steps.
- Technology has improved the quality of family life.

QUESTIONS

Mrs Smith is now in full-time employment. She works from 9 am to 5 pm. The family must all help in managing the home. The two younger children (aged eight and ten) have to be collected from school at 3 pm. The teenager arrives home at 4 pm.

1 Draw up a task schedule for the Smith family for one weekday evening. It should include making the evening meal, cleaning the kitchen and bathroom, doing the laundry, and buying the food.
2 Look at this picture. It shows a kitchen in the 1900s. Discuss how technology has improved the quality of life within the home since the time when this kitchen was being used.

Living space

Living conditions in the home

Living conditions within the home affect the **physical**, **emotional**, **intellectual** and **social** wellbeing of the family members.

POSITIVE LIVING CONDITIONS	NEGATIVE LIVING CONDITIONS
Physical	
warmth good food space comfortable surroundings safe, well-maintained furnishings and equipment	damp poor-quality food cramped conditions squalid unsafe equipment
Emotional	
love and attention security protection	emotional neglect insecure abuse
Intellectual	
books/toys, etc. for children recreation praise and encouragement	lack of stimulation lack of opportunities criticism
Social	
privacy spending time together as a family good routine discipline	no privacy neglected/isolated lack of organization lack of discipline

Effects on children and other family members

Physical needs

Positive
- healthy
- develop normally
- have a sense of wellbeing.

Negative
- susceptible to illness
- stunted growth
- chest infections
- colds
- lack energy
- lethargic
- over/underweight
- low self-esteem.

Emotional needs

Positive
- secure
- happy
- well-adjusted
- good self-image
- able to form stable relationships
- mature.

Negative
- insecure
- unhappy
- slow to talk
- slow to walk
- withdrawn
- timid
- shy
- lack confidence
- poor communication
- unable to form relationships.

Intellectual needs

Positive
- easily stimulated
- keen to learn
- curious
- interested
- easily motivated
- good attitude to learning.

Negative
- slow to talk and read
- slow learner
- uninterested
- difficult to motivate
- low achiever
- troublesome
- attention seeking
- low attention span.

Social needs

Positive
- able to communicate with others
- pleasant to deal with
- socially adjusted
- good self-image
- confident
- self-disciplined.

Negative
- loner
- poor social skills
- lack of confidence
- poor self-image.

Living space and family needs

Living space may require alterations as the needs and lifestyle of the family change.

A house provides shelter from the elements, privacy and space for each individual member.

Whilst most houses now provide the basic requirements of kitchen, bathroom, and bedrooms, these vary in size and layout. The choice of home is determined by the:
- number in the family
- age-group
- personal needs of the family.

Living space required by family groups

Young adult living alone or newly married couple

Basic requirements for the groups are similar – one bedroom, bathroom, kitchen and living space.

Married couple with young children

Basic requirements for this group are *two* bedrooms, bathroom, kitchen, *more* living space.

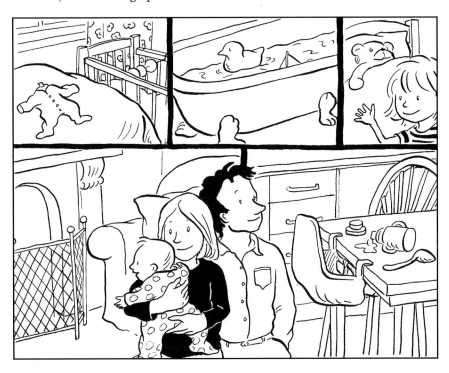

Married couple with teenagers (boys and girls)

Basic requirements for this group are *at least three* bedrooms (one for parents, one for boys and one for girls), bathroom, kitchen, *study space, more living space* and *dining space.*

Elderly

Basic requirements for this group are bedroom, bathroom, kitchen and living space. Also a *smaller house* that is *easy to heat, clean and maintain* and *easy to get around.*

Special circumstances

At any stage alterations may be necessary to accommodate people with particular needs, e.g. elderly or disabled people: handrails on stairs or bathroom, wider doors, ramps, plugs at waist level, stair lifts, good lighting, special fitments for baths, shower and toilet, special taps for sinks and hand basins, window and door handles altered to suit individual needs.

Some of these alterations are paid for by the DSS.

SUMMARY

- Living conditions can affect the family in a positive or negative way.
- As the family progresses through the lifecycle, its needs change and living space can or should be altered.

● ●

QUESTIONS

1 What are the possible effects of poor living conditions on a pre-school child?

2 Suggest how a home could be adapted to meet the needs of:

   a a family with a disabled child in a wheelchair

   b an elderly couple.

Appendices

Coursework tasks: Model

Coursework is an integral part of GCSE examinations. The model below has been designed to:

  a explain each stage of the process
  b provide a worked example
  c provide two other titles that the process can be applied to.

The coursework section included in this book is in line with the GCSE Home Economics Syllabus offered by CCEA.

Task title

This is usually written as a case study. The task presents a scenario which includes certain problems or specific situations. A number of issues relevant to the task are identified for students to consider. The outcome of the task must be completed as a solution to a problem and involves practical work, usually in the form of preparing snacks or meals.

The process

STEP 1: Identify issues

This means selecting the main issues to be considered from the task title. The issues must be briefly explained, highlighting who will be affected and in what way. Related issues may be clustered. Issues may be written as bullet points or prose.

STEP 2: Assemble and consider relevant information – analyse viewpoints

Each key issue or cluster of related issues must be developed through the selective use of relevant primary or secondary sources such as textbooks, interviews, videos, TV programmes, questionnaires, magazines, class notes, pamphlets, computer programs. Students must obtain and present the viewpoints of at least two people on the issues associated with the task. The differing opinions and viewpoints, including the student's own viewpoint, should be analysed and an explanation or justification offered for these veiwpoints.

STEP 3: Arrive at and justify personal viewpoint

This means stating one's personal viewpoint (opinion) in light of findings from Step 2. Personal viewpoints should be justified.

STEP 4: Make decisions, plan and take a course of action

A range of meals should be suggested, based on research from STEPS 2 and 3. These should be evaluated in the light of the task title, taking into account the issues discussed. A final choice should be made and costed. Reasons for the choice should be given and a plan of action drawn up.

STEP 5: Practical

The practical is the execution of the chosen dishes, using a high level of competence, showing a range of skills and efficiency in the management of time and resources.

STEP 6: Evaluation of application of process and outcome

Each step should be evaluated, highlighting strengths and weaknesses of the work throughout, indicating where and how improvements could be made.

STEP 7: Bibliography

All resources and sources should be acknowledged throughout the text and at the end. The bibliography should be written as follows: title of book or article, author.

Worked example of coursework

Task title

Mr and Mrs Jones have two children, Megan, aged 13 years and James, aged six years. Mr Jones is overweight. Mrs Jones has a part-time job and finds mealtimes rushed. Megan is often tired and lethargic.

Advise Mrs Jones on how to plan and organize family meals.

Select and evaluate a range of meals to be eaten by this family over a two-day period.

Prepare a two-course evening meal suitable for all members of the family.

STEP 1

The main issues to consider could be:

- Mr Jones is overweight
- Mrs Jones is rushed
- Megan is a female adolescent, possibly anaemic
- James is a growing boy
- Mr Jones and Megan have particular nutritional needs
- strategies for managing meal preparation.

STEP 2

The main issues have to be researched in:
secondary sources
textbooks
food tables
information about dietary problems
information about dietary management
recipes for quick meals
information about convenience foods
dietary goals and labour-saving equipment
primary sources
interviews with a housewife and/or working mother
someone with dietary problems similar to Mr Jones
dual earners with similar lifestyle.

STEP 3

Having considered information from both primary and secondary sources, the student's own view should now be given on how Mrs Jones could plan and organize family meals, given her situation and her family's needs.

STEP 4

Plan and cost a range of meals considering the needs of this family. Evaluate and give reasons for their selection. Make a final choice, justify and draw up a plan of action, for example:
Shepherd's pie
- iron content for Megan
- could be made the previous night
- low fat mince could be used for Mr Jones
- suits the whole family's taste
- could use convenience foods such as 'smash'
- involve other family members in the preparation of the meal.

STEP 5

Carry out practical work demonstrating a range of skills.

STEP 6

Evaluate each step of the process above.
Ask questions about each step in the process, for example:
- Did I clearly understand all the relevant issues?
- Did I make good use of primary and secondary sources?
- Could I make any improvements?
- Was my choice of meals suitable?

STEP 7

Acknowledge primary and secondary sources in the bibliography, for example:
<u>Title of book</u>   Author

Coursework title

Mary, whose first husband died, has a son aged 13. She is now happily married to a widower, John, who has a daughter aged 15.

The family are financially secure.

There are positive and negative aspects of a second marriage like this. Each child has moved from being an only child to a shared situation.

What conflict situations arise and what strategies could be used to resolve them?

Suggest a range of meals the teenagers could prepare for a two-course evening meal for their parents.

Plan, make and evaluate one of these meals.

Coursework title

Peter and Jane Smith have been married for two years. They live in a rented apartment which is partly furnished. Jane is in full-time employment and they both have expensive tastes.

The Smiths regularly use credit cards to purchase goods. Peter has just been made redundant after six years with his firm.

They now realize that they will have financial problems. This is the first major crisis in their marriage and it has put a strain on their relationship. Suggest strategies on how they should manage their problems, considering meals as one way they could economize.

Plan and make a two-course evening meal that Peter could prepare.

Sources of support provided for families

AA
152 Lisburn Road
Belfast
01232 681084

Action Cancer
127 Marlborough Park South
Belfast BT9 6HW
01232 661081

Action Multiple Sclerosis
Knockbracken Healthcare Park
Belfast BT8 8BH
01232 790707

Adopt
2 Windsor Road
Belfast
01232 382353

Age Concern Ireland
3 Lower Crescent
Belfast BT7 1NR
01232 245729

Aids Helpline
7 James South
Belfast BT2 8DN
01232 249268
Freephone 0800 137437

All Children Together
13 University Street
Belfast
01232 327335

Ards Society for Mentally Handicapped Children
203 South Street
Newtonards
01247 815363

Arthritis and Rheumatism Council
17 Cleland Park
South Bangor
01247 463109

ASH (smoking campaign)
5–11 Mortimer Street
London W1N 7RH

Association for Mental Health
80 University Street
Belfast BT7 1HE
01232 328474

Association for Sick Children (in hospital)
Argyle House
29–31 Euston Road
London NW1 2SD
0171 833 2041

Association for Spina Bifida
73 New Row
Coleraine
01625 51522

Association of Breast Feeding Mothers
Sydenham Green Health Centre
Holmshaw Close
London SE26 ATH
0181 778 4796

Barnardos – Child Care
542–544 Upper Newtownards Road
Belfast
01232 672336

Blackstaff Common Health Project
Olympia Community Centre
Boucher Road
Belfast

The Blind Centre for Northern Ireland
70 North Road
Belfast BT5 5NJ
01232 654366

Body Positive
Bryson House
Bedford Street
Belfast
01232 235515

Bradbury Surgical Ltd
137 Hillsborough Old Road
Lisburn
01846 605445

British Dental Health Association
131 Ballygowan Road
Banbridge
018206 27270

British Diabetic Association
257 Lisburn Road
Belfast 9
01232 666646

British Epilepsy Association
Knockbracken Healthcare Park
Southfield Road
Belfast 8
01232 799355

British Red Cross Society
87 University Street
Belfast BT7
01232 246400
01232 322325

Catholic Family Care Society Northern Ireland
511 Ormeau Road
Belfast
01232 691133

Catholic Marriage Advisory Council
01232 233002

Chest, Heart and Stroke
21 Dublin Road
Belfast BT2 7FT
01232 320184

Child Care International
248 Woodstock Road
Belfast 6
01232 732003

Child Care (NI)
11 University Street
Belfast 7
01232 234499

Child Care Resource Centre
49a Dhu Varren
Portrush
01265 824 698

Child Poverty Action Group
12 Queen Street
Londonderry
01504 267777

Childline
121 Spencer Road
Derry
01504 311555

Citizens Advice Bureau
1/3 Guildhall Street
Derry
01504 362444

Citizens Advice Bureau (Northern Ireland Association of . . .)
6 Callender Street
Belfast 1
01232 243196

Community Relations Information
6 Murray Street
Belfast 1
01232 311881

Community Relations in School
Unit 8
R. J. Hall Industrial Estate
Wilson Street
Belfast 13
01232 313123

Concern Worldwide
47 Frederick Street
Belfast
01232 331100

Consumer Advice Centre
6 Callendar Street
Belfast
01232 328260

Council for the Homeless (Northern Ireland)
153 University Street
Belfast 7
01232 246440

CRUSE
Regional Headquarters
Knockbracken Healthcare Park
Belfast 8
01232 792419

Cystic Fibrosis Research Trust
20 Bryansburn Road
Bangor
01232 272781

Dairy Council for Northern Ireland
456 Antrim Road
Belfast
01232 770113

Deaf Self Help Society
6 Ballyfore Park
Newtown Abbey
Belfast
01232 853600

Derry Community Social Services Centre
1a High Street
Derry
01504 363581

Derry Woman's Centre
7 London Street
Derry
01504 267672

Disability Action
2 Annadale Avenue
Belfast
01232 491011

Disablecare
339–343 Donegall Road
Belfast
01232 230744

Downs Syndrome Association
84 The Beeches
Portadown
01762 392209

Electricity Advice Centre
Campsie Industrial Estate
Courtald Way
Derry
01504 860707

Energy Action (Northern Ireland)
8–10 Exchange Place
Belfast
01232 333790

Equal Opportunities Commission
Chamber of Commerce House
Great Victoria Street
Belfast 2
01232 242752

Extern Organization
1 Albert Square
Belfast 1
01232 240900

Extra Care for Elderly People Ltd
Extra Care House
1 Wellington Park
Belfast 9
01232 683273

Family and Child Care Team
Castlerock Road
Coleraine
01265 52221

Family and Poverty Relief Association
72 High Street
Belfast
01232 313007

Family Caring Centre
The
5 Somerset Park
Antrim
018494 64619

Family Caring Trust
44 Rathfriland Road
Newry
0165 64174

Family Support Project
13 Dunluce Court
Derry
01504 269883

Fold Housing Association
3 Redburn Square
Holywood
Co. Down BT18 9HZ
01232 428314

Fold Trust
1 Catherine Street
Limavady
Co. Derry
015047 66865

Foyle, Homeless Action and Advice Service
23 Bishop Street
Londonderry
01504 266115

Gamblers, Anon
Resource Centre
Carnhill
Derry
01504 351329

Gas Board
01232 451147

Gingerbread (Northern Ireland)
169 University Street
Belfast
01232 234568

Haemophilia Society
6 Kilcoole Park
Belfast 14
01232 729559
or
22 Bishop Street
Derry
01504 668725

Health Promotion Agency for Northern Ireland
18 Ormeau Avenue
Belfast
01232 311611

Help the Aged
Leslie House
Shaftsbury Square
Belfast
01232 230666

HMSO
Chichester Street
Belfast

Home Start Consultancy
133 Bloomfield Avenue
Belfast 5
01232 460772

Inner City Trust
13 Pump Street
Derry
01504 260329

Institute for Counselling and Personal Development
22 York Street
Belfast 15
01232 330996

LIFE
Pregnancy Care Centre
Bryson House
28 Bedford Street
Belfast
01232 249414
or
3 Customs House Street
Derry
01504 264751
or
Derrygonnelly
0156564 725

MARC
Money Relationships Counselling
16 Donegall Square North
Belfast
01232 240694

ME Association
Bryson House
28 Bedford Street
Belfast
01232 439831

Mencap
4 Annadale Avenue
Belfast
01232 691351

Multiple Sclerosis Action Group
Actionville
Purdysburn Estate
Belfast 8
01232 790707

National Deaf Children's Society
15 Dufferin Street
Belfast
01232 313170

Northern Ireland Association for Mental Health
80 University Street
Belfast
01232 328474

Northern Ireland Child Minding Association
17a Court Street
Newtownards
01247 811015

Northern Ireland Council on Alcohol
Belfast
01232 664434

Northern Ireland Dyslexia Association
28 Bedford Street
Belfast 2
01232 243100

Northern Ireland Mother and Baby Appeal
15 Stranmillis Road
Belfast
01232 667166

Northern Ireland Pre-School Playgroups Association
Belfast
01232 6628265

Northern Ireland Sports Council
01232 381222

NSPCC
16/20 Rosemary Street
Belfast
01232 240311

Oxfam
PO Box 70
52 Dublin Road
Belfast
01232 230220

PACE
103 University Street
Belfast
01232 232864

PAPA (Autism)
623 Lisburn Road
Belfast
01232 660891

Physically Handicapped and Able-bodied Club (PHAB)
6 Pump Street
Derry
01504 371030
and
Mourn Villa
Knockbracken Healthcare Park
Belfast
01232 796565

PRAXIS
29 Lisburn Road
Belfast
01232 234555
or
16 Bishop Street
Derry
01504 308020

Relate
Belfast
01232 323454

Samaritans
01232 664422

Save the Children
15 Richmond Park
Belfast 10
01232 620000

SENSE
41 Edenvale Avenue
Carrickfergus
01960 363638

SHELTER
165 University Street
Belfast
01232 247752

SIMON Community
57 Fitzroy Avenue
Belfast
01232 232888

Society for the Protection of the Unborn Child (SPUC)
2 Veryan Gardens
Belfast
01232 778018

Ulster Deaf Sports Council
5 College Square North
Belfast
01232 312255

Ulster Institute for the Deaf
Wilton House
5 College Square North
Belfast
01232 321733

UNICEF (UK)
Plot 46
Brackenridge Estate
Donaghadee
01247 884335

We Care
Third World Organization
42 Springfield Road
Belfast
01232 243263

Well Woman Centre
17 Queen Street
Derry
01504 360777

Young Peoples Centre
10 College Gardens
Belfast
01232 681800

Glossary of terms used in coursework and examination papers

account for	explain, give the reason for
analyse	examine in detail; break down into simple parts
assess	give your judgement on the merit of something; give your opinion of the quality of something
calculate	work out
critically assess	judge the quality of something (good and bad) and give reasons or justify your opinion
comment on	write concise, explanatory notes on, or about, a topic; give an opinion on something
compare/contrast	look for similarities and differences
consider	think about something in order to understand it or decide about it; weigh the merit of something
conclude	bring to an end
conclusion	overall findings, judgement on preceding work
data	information displayed
describe in detail	give a full account of something, with examples of the procedure
define	give the exact meaning
discuss	investigate or examine by argument, giving reasons for and against; it may or may not be necessary to come to a conclusion
evaluate	appraise, state or judge the advantages or disadvantages of something
examine	look at or study something closely to find out the facts
execution	carrying out; putting into action
explain	make plain or clear; interpret and account for; make one's meaning clear
identify	name and/or select, pick out
illustrate	make clear by the use of diagrams, pictures and examples; explain or clarify by the use of concrete examples
issues	the main points to consider, they emerge from work
justify	give reasons/evidence to defend your choice/opinion
list	name facts as short points rather than in sentences

outcome	final result
outline	give main features, summary of main points
process	a logical sequence, course of action, series of stages, progress, course
state	give the relevant fact(s) briefly and to the point
summary	a brief account of findings
viewpoint	opinion, standpoint